VISUAL SIMULATION

VISUAL SIMULATION

A User's Guide for Architects, Engineers, and Planners

Stephen R. J. Sheppard, Ph.D

VNR VAN NOSTRAND REINHOLD
_____ New York

To Linda,
who, until now, has never known her husband without this book
lurking unfinished in the background, and who,
for her perseverance, really deserves the credit
for it being completed at all.

Frontispiece: A new commercial development with its sign still in place, providing a
rare opportunity to compare the simulated with the real.

Library of Congress Catalog Card Number 89-30620
ISBN 0-442-27827-6

Printed in the United States of America

Van Nostrand Reinhold
115 Fifth Avenue
New York, New York 10003

Van Nostrand Reinhold International Company Limited
11 New Fetter Lane
London EC4P 4EE, England

Van Nostrand Reinhold
480 La Trobe Street
Melbourne, Victoria 3000, Australia

Macmillan of Canada
Division of Canada Publishing Corporation
164 Commander Boulevard
Agincourt, Ontario M1S 3C7, Canada

16 15 14 13 12 11 10 9 8 7 6 5 4 3 2 1

Library of Congress Cataloging-in-Publication Data

Sheppard, S. R. J. (Stephen Richard John), 1952–
    Visual simulation : a user's guide for architects, engineers, and
planners / by Stephen R. J. Sheppard.
        p. cm.
    Bibliography: p.
    Includes index.
    ISBN 0-442-27827-6
    1. Architecture—Simulation methods.   2. Landscape architecture—
Simulation methods.   3. City planning—Simulation methods.
4. Engineering--Simulation methods.   I. Title.
NA2750.S54   1989
720'.28—dc19   89-30620
                                                              CIP

CONTENTS

ACKNOWLEDGMENTS

Any book that takes as long to produce as this one did, and has gone through as many iterations, trails a long list of people who have helped shape and support its development.

First, I must acknowledge the members of my Doctoral Dissertation Committee at University of California, Berkeley whose own research and personal encouragement of mine laid the groundwork for this book: Professor R. Burton Litton Jr., the late Donald Appleyard, and Professor Kenneth Craik.

I am indebted to the various professionals and academics who have reviewed the different drafts of the manuscript and contributed much to my thought process: Dr. Len Ortolano, Department of Civil Engineering, Stanford University; Arlene Evans, Marin County Planning Commission; Tim Tetherow, Dames & Moore, Denver; Hartmut Gerdes, Square One Film + Video, San Francisco; Professor Ken Craik, Department of Psychology, U.C. Berkeley; Bob Itami, Department of Renewable Natural Resources, University of Arizona; Bob Ross, Chief Landscape Architect for the U.S. Forest Service, Washington, D.C.; and Professor John Lyle, University of California, Pomona. In addition, I owe thanks to Greg McPhearson (University of Arizona), Rick Smardon (SUNY Syracuse), Rob Thayer (U.C. Davis), and the staff of the Landscape Architecture Foundation for helpful advice on publishing.

My thanks also go to the staff of Dames & Moore (and, formerly, WIRTH Environmental Services), who tolerated my extracurricular activities and provided much-needed logistical support. In particular, I would like to recognize Shirley Wiley who over the years orchestrated so many clean drafts from multicolored montaged scribbles; Denny Papilion who produced many of the original graphics while sustaining a heavy workload; and the Visual Design Services group in San Francisco for their loyalty. Many other people at Dames & Moore have been helpful in large and small ways, and I am very grateful for their contributions to ''the book that would not die.''

I must thank too the numerous people and organizations who have provided graphics, quotations, and other materials for the book. Their efforts and willingness to contribute are much appreciated. A full list of credits appears on pp. 211–212.

Lastly, I would like to thank the staff of Van Nostrand Reinhold for their patience and faith in a first-time author who seldom met his deadlines.

INTRODUCTION

In 1977, when I first came to Berkeley (where this book had its beginning), "visual resources" and "landscape values" were still fairly new buzzwords. It was clear that the public cared a lot about the appearance of their surroundings and that government and the business community were being forced to recognize this. My interest in this phenomenon led me to look at master plans and environmental impact reports for new development projects in California and elsewhere. These reports often represent the crucial stage for project approval and design decisions. I found an astonishing variety of graphics showing what the proposed project would look like, ranging from plan view only, through crude perspectives, to highly sophisticated computer graphics. There appeared to be no consistency, no rules, and no intrinsic logic behind this pattern. While criteria, statements, and findings in the text of environmental assessments often were pored over with a fine-tooth comb, no one seemed to care very much whether or how illustrative graphics were used. Much was left to chance. Did it matter?

If, indeed, a picture is worth a thousand words, did it not make sense to devote at least as much attention to the pictures as to the words? Was this blind acceptance one of the reasons that, in spite of the planning and approval process, so many projects when built turn out to be surprisingly ugly, inappropriate, or simply unimaginative?

On digging deeper, of course, it was obvious that some people did care a great deal about how the appearance of projects was depicted. Developers strove to give their buildings the right image in public relations brochures and design submittals. Students in architecture and landscape design devoted long hours through the night to perfecting their design renderings. Planners admitted to being prejudiced against all presentation drawings. Members of the public complained about dishonest or useless portrayals of controversial projects. Clearly, some people did believe that the way pictures were used could make a big difference to the fate of proposed projects.

Here then was a rich vein of contradiction, worthy of study. Oddly, there had been very little prior research that looked at the influence of pictures on the planning and approval of actual development projects. Government agencies were starting to ask the question, "What do we need in order to review projects better?" When they

1

asked, "How do we know whether to trust the simulations we get?" no one could advise them. There were no professional or local standards for producing pictures of future projects, and no comprehensive guidelines.

Over the subsequent ten years of trying to help fill this gap, I often worried about the timeliness of the final product. Would time and experience make a book such as this irrelevant? I need not have been concerned. Even in the San Francisco Bay area, where planning is relatively sophisticated and much relevant research in visual simulation has been conducted, the problems, questions, and needs are still much the same. The possibilities of presentation media have expanded, with exciting advances in computers and video, but problems and arguments continue to surround the images used in project planning. In fact, if anything, the technological advances of today make it all the more urgent to establish sound underlying principles for simulation.

Any book that reviews the state of the art in a given profession is, by nature, critical in tone. If everyone who prepared simulations did so perfectly, there would be no reason for a book such as this. In order to show the difference between a good simulation and a bad one, it is necessary to illustrate with actual examples. However, it is not the author's intent to criticize individuals or organizations who have prepared less than perfect simulations; rather, the intent is to show typical problems, and to explain why they continually recur. For every simulation in this book that illustrates a potential problem, I am certain that I could find any number of substitute simulations with similar problems, prepared by others.

There are, as will be demonstrated, many reasons why simulations turn out to be incorrect or ineffective. Some of these reasons are totally beyond the control of those preparing the simulation at the time. This should be borne in mind when perusing the simulation examples illustrated in the book. Furthermore, the quality of simulations produced ten years ago, as were some of the examples used in this book, is no indication of the quality of simulations produced today by the same people or organizations. It should also be noted that, in a few instances, I have used simulations taken out of context to illustrate a particular problem, even though they may have served their purpose admirably in the context in which they were used. The reader should not assume, therefore, that because a certain simulation exhibits a particular problem in the author's opinion, it was necessarily a bad or misleading simulation. The truth is far more complex than that, as will be discussed.

Consequently, I hope that those who supplied examples of simulations to illustrate the book will forgive any apparently critical comments, and recognize the value of their contribution in helping to advance the state of the art.

Throughout the developed nations and increasingly in other parts of the world, concern for aesthetics and the quality of life is growing, and the financial, legal, and cultural stakes in land-use decisions have risen considerably. Against that background, it is hoped that readers of this book can help to improve the way pictures influence decisions in planning and design, and thereby in some small way perhaps improve both the planning process itself and the quality of the future designed landscape.

Chapter 1

DEFINITIONS AND OBJECTIVES

Suppose that someone proposes to build a housing development, cut down some trees, or open a quarry near a residential area. One of the first things the residents would probably want to know is: "What will it look like?" Depending upon local planning procedures and the level of interest among the people, they might take a look at the plans. They might even have the appearance of the proposed project described to them at a public meeting or in an environmental impact report. The item that would create the strongest impression, however, is likely to be a picture of the proposed project.

This book deals with the way such pictures are used, and should be used, in the planning of projects or developments on the land.

Pictures that illustrate or simulate the appearance of a proposed design or construction project are called *visual simulations*. Examples of visual simulations that are commonly used to portray new projects include

- perspective drawings (often referred to as "artist's concepts," "artist's impressions," sketches, renderings, or architectural illustrations) (Fig. 1-1)

Figure 1-1. Perspective rendering of proposed resort complex.

- scale models (Fig. 1-2)
- photo simulations (see cover illustration), including photomontage, photo renderings, retouching, and photo overlays

Among newer techniques beginning to be more widely used in depicting projects are

- computer-aided design/drafting (CADD) graphics (Fig. 1-3)
- video image processing or videosimulation (Fig. 1-4 and Plate 1)

These techniques, including the materials and equipment used to create the picture, are called *simulation media.*

All of these simulations are capable of showing a view of something *in perspective,* the way we see real environments: with an impression of depth, as viewed from a particular position or viewpoint. This is a characteristic not shared by diagrams, plans, cross sections, elevations, or axonometric drawings, which are formal graphic conventions showing a single, limited facet of a project (Fig. 1-5*a*). While these can simulate an object, they do not simulate an actual view of that object.

The unique advantage of perspective in a picture is that it places objects into a clear three-dimensional relationship with other objects and with the surrounding context or setting (Fig. 1-5*b*). This overall scene of project and context constitutes the visual environment or *landscape* that we would see.

Visualizing environments is a critical concept: we should not visualize just a project or de-

Figure 1-2. Scale model of geothermal power plant.

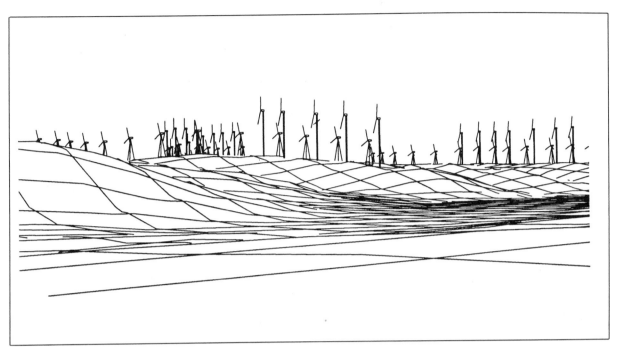

Figure 1-3. Computer graphic of proposed wind turbines.

Figure 1-4 *(above)*. Videosimulation of an existing building superimposed on a different site.

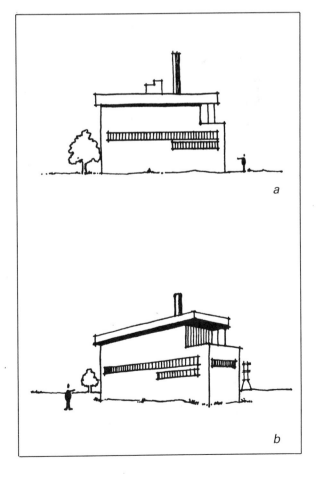

a

b

Figure 1-5 *(right)*. The difference between an elevation and a perspective drawing: elevation *(a)*; perspective drawing *(b)*.

sign, but the project in its context—the whole environment as changed by the project.

The simulations that concern us differ from ordinary landscape paintings or photographs in that they show something that does not yet exist at the time the picture is created. They show planned projects, or, more correctly, planned projects in their future setting; in other words, they help us visualize future landscapes.

For the purposes of this guide, therefore, simulations are defined as

visual pictures or images of proposed projects or future conditions, shown in perspective views in the context of actual sites.

Simulations are a highly useful and potentially very powerful tool in project planning and review, because they allow for more informed decisions. The value of simulation lies in translating a set of plans or blueprints into a picture of the proposed project, in an understandable context, so that information can be more clearly presented before projects are built. This information is of value to project sponsors, designers, reviewers, and the public. The power of simulation as a communications device follows from the importance of people's perceptions or mental images of a project in shaping their decisions about it.

Thus, it is not surprising that in recent years the upsurge in environmental regulation and public participation in project planning has been accompanied by an increase in demand for visual simulations. At the same time, many new methods of simulation have become available. The time is ripe, therefore, for us to step back and review how simulations *are* prepared and used, and how they *should be* prepared and used. While it is clearly important that so powerful a communications tool should be used to its full potential, it is also vital that its power not be misused. Information presented in simulations ought to be correct, in order that decisions supported by simulations are fair and unbiased.

Although there are many texts describing particular simulation techniques, there is no comprehensive manual or set of established principles or guidelines to aid those who are involved with visual simulation, despite Appleyard's seminal work on the subject.[1] How are people to know whether a simulation is good or bad for their purposes? The aim of this book, therefore, is to encourage and facilitate the correct use of simulations in appropriate aspects of project planning and review.

The specific objectives of the book are

1. to explain the various roles that simulations can assume in project planning and review, and the advantages to be gained by their use in these roles
2. to provide insight on the influence of simulations on the opinions and decisions of people, together with the potential consequences (good and bad) for public acceptability of projects and the project approval process
3. to present a set of principles for fair and effective simulation
4. to develop from these principles a set of practical guidelines and policies for those who produce or use simulations in project planning and review

The underlying premise is that simulations are needed but they must be good simulations. This may seem obvious, but, in fact, many people will believe what they see in a picture without knowing anything about how it was created. Particularly with today's high-tech wizardry, it can be impossible for the average person to tell what is real and what is false, what is correct and what is exaggerated. That a simulation is good is not always self-evident.

Good simulations can only be assured by the process of creating them. Visual simulations can and should be used in a rational, systematic, balanced manner, and not to serve special interests. One of the purposes of this book is to show that there need be nothing magical or mysterious about producing simulations, and that, properly used, they should be neither distrusted nor glorified. They should be a routine and accepted aid in project decision-making, available to and understood by people who need not be artists or experts.

The book is intended primarily for people who are concerned with some aspect of project design, planning, or review. The definition of "project" is interpreted broadly. A *project* may be any of man's activities that affects the outdoor environment: the result of engineering, architecture, landscape architecture, or land management. Typical projects covered in this book include high-rise buildings, residential developments, parks, highways, transit systems, power lines, power plants, mining, reservoirs, and land-fills. Any of these can have substantial environmental and perceived impacts. This guide is intended to apply both to major high-profile projects that may call for special attention, and to the routine small projects that many planners and designers deal with every day.

Much of the use of simulations focuses upon the appearance of projects and on aesthetic considerations. However, neither the potential of simulations nor the content of this book is limited to purely aesthetic applications. For example, simulations can help to explain how a project would work and illustrate physical problems or advantages of a design, such as proximity to other buildings or roads. They can also communicate other sensory characteristics, such as traffic noise or the coolness of shade.

The book is designed for three main types of reader (Fig. 1-6):

- *Preparers* of simulations (Fig. 1-6a)—those who themselves create or help to produce visual simulations

- *Presenters* of simulations (Fig 1-6b)—those who present simulations to an audience or use them to communicate information
- *Interpreters* of simulations (Fig. 1-6c)—the audience that views simulations, reacts to them, and obtains some kind of information from them

b

c

a

Figure 1-6. Simulation users: preparers *(a)*; presenters *(b)*; interpreters *(c)*.

In many cases, however, these categories are not mutually exclusive. Preparers often interpret and present their own simulations, and need to know how their simulations will be interpreted by others; interpreters need to know something about how the simulations were created. They are all users of simulations in some sense, whether it be to produce, communicate, or receive visual information.

The types of simulation-users who are typically involved in project design, planning, or review and who could benefit from the guidelines in this manual, include the following:

- project designers, such as landscape architects, architects, engineers, or land managers
- professional illustrators and model-builders
- environmental consultants responsible for environmental impact and planning studies
- government regulatory staff, planners, and land managers responsible for planning and project review
- planning commissioners, city council members, and other elected or appointed officials who make decisions on design review, project approval, and permitting
- community groups, special-interest groups, and members of the public who might be affected by a project

The guide is intended also to be a source of information for students in architecture, landscape architecture, civil engineering, community and regional planning, graphics, illustration, and perceptual or environmental psychology.

Many of those who encounter simulations and who are potential readers of this guide have little knowledge of the simulation process and its possible consequences. The structure of the book is, therefore, planned to begin with the basics, work up through applications and principles for simulation use, and culminate in practical guidelines and policies for those who actually use simulations in their work or communities.

First, it is necessary to understand the need for simulations and the potential breadth of their application. Chapter 2, Applications of Visual Simulation, outlines how simulations fit into the project planning process, together with the benefits of using simulations as part of this process.

It is also necessary to review briefly the background to the use of simulations in *visual resource assessment,* which is the mechanism by which aesthetic considerations are systematically incorporated into planning. Chapter 3, The Role of Simulation in Visual Analysis, does this. Readers already familiar with project planning and visual analysis may wish to skip Chapters 2 and 3 and proceed directly to Chapter 4. However, some understanding of visual analysis, as described in Chapter 3, is advantageous in explaining the basis for some of the concepts and principles of simulation discussed later. Indeed, it is the author's contention that good simulation cannot be carried out without an understanding of at least the basics of visual analysis.

Chapter 4, Fundamentals and Problems in Simulation Use, explains the fundamental objectives inherent in good simulation, and what makes a good or bad simulation. It also reviews the major problems that occur with simulations as they are used in practice.

Chapter 5, The Simulation Process, outlines the steps in the normal simulation process, which mark the stages at which the quality of simulation is decided.

Chapter 6, Principles for Simulation Use, provides broad principles for fair and effective simulation, and illustrates specific problems that can be encountered in simulation use when these principles are not followed.

Chapter 7, Practical Guidelines, provides techniques for those who routinely use simulations. The first two sections supply simple guidelines on planning and preparing simulations in accordance with the principles established earlier; these guidelines are intended to help preparers with varying degrees of experience to avoid the problems described in Chapters 4 and 6. The third section of this chapter suggests guidelines on presenting simulations. The fourth section provides guidelines for those who interpret simulations and wish to judge or appraise the quality of a simulation; these guidelines are intended to help interpreters of simulations to detect problems of the type discussed in Chapters 4 and 6. The final section provides guidance on postconstruction appraisal of simulations.

Chapter 8, Case Studies in Simulation Appraisal, further illustrates how the guidelines on appraisal of simulations may be implemented, by means of three case studies in which the merits of simulation example are analyzed.

Chapter 9, Policies for Simulation, provides policy directions for agencies considering the adoption of guidelines, requirements, or professional standards for simulation in everyday planning.

A Glossary of terms used in this guide and in simulation practice is provided, as well as a Bibliography for background reading and for those who wish to learn more about particular simulation media or simulation research. A Technical Supplement to the guidelines in Chapter 7 is provided in Appendix A for users who intend to specialize in the practice of simulation and are interested in the details and more complex aspects of specific procedures. It should be stressed, however, that this is first and foremost a guide to principles and approaches to simulation, rather than a step-by-step instruction manual for individual simulation media. The references in the Bibliography should be consulted for such information on simulation techniques.

Some information on simulation costs is provided in Appendix B. Appendix C presents a model ordinance for agencies interested in requiring simulations on project applications, together with an abbreviated set of guidelines that could readily be adopted or recommended by agencies.

The contents of this guide are drawn primarily from research conducted by the author at the Department of Landscape Architecture, University of California, Berkeley.[2] The study examined and tested simulations as an influence on people's reactions to projects. This research involved review of literature related to simulation theory and practice; a survey and analysis of typical visual simulations used in project planning and review in North America; comparison of projects as simulated with the same projects as built; and analysis of people's responses to both simulations and views of the actual projects. The research was designed to provide information drawn from and directly applicable to the real world of project planning, where an understanding of the factors influencing the public acceptability of projects is crucial. A summary of the approach and methods used in this research is given for the reader's information in Appendix D.

The information in this guide also reflects the experience of the author and colleagues in over 13 years of preparing and using simulations in public and private practice. Much insight and information has been gained through informal but highly valuable discussions held with other practicing environmental professionals, illustrators, developers, and community members concerned with project-related issues.

The guidelines presented here are a first step in addressing the problems and needs associated with the use of visual simulations as a tool in project review and planning. Much is still unknown about how and why simulations affect people's judgments. The guidelines are suggested as a cautionary measure urgently needed in simulation use. They reflect our current knowledge and most plausible theories. They may need to be revised as new research results become available, as new technologies evolve, and as experience with simulations grows.

REFERENCES

1. Appleyard, D. 1977. "Understanding professional media." In *Human Behavior and Environment,* Vol. 1, ed. Altman and Wohlwill, New York: Plenum Press, pp. 43–88.

2. Sheppard, S. R. J. 1982. "Landscape portrayals: their use, accuracy, and validity in simulating proposed landscape changes." Ph.D. diss., University of California, Berkeley.

Chapter **2**

APPLICATIONS OF VISUAL SIMULATION

This chapter explains the situations in which visual simulations are used or might be used to advantage, and, particularly, how they fit into the process of project planning. For the purposes of this guide, the term *project planning* is used to cover all phases of project design, development, evaluation, and approval. Before the potential applications of simulation can be discussed, it is necessary to understand the basic planning process that provides the context for simulation use. Later in this chapter, the roles that simulations can play in the most crucial phases of project planning are outlined and the consequences of such use considered.

THE PROJECT PLANNING PROCESS

The ways in which construction or land management projects are planned vary considerably. Nevertheless, in Western nations it is possible to identify a number of generic steps in the planning process, not all of which may be undertaken for a particular project. Depending upon such factors as the legislative requirements of government, the environmental awareness of the public, and

the attitudes of the project sponsor, some or all of the activities listed in the simplified process chart in Figure 2-1 may occur. These activities include initial project planning, preliminary design, project review and environmental impact assessment (if required), project approval, detailed design, implementation, and monitoring. People involved in the process may include developers, project designers (engineers, architects, landscape architects), staff of government review agencies, the public, and other local interest groups.

In fact, there are many more possible steps and points of contact between the parties involved than are suggested in Figure 2-1. For instance, developers of large or complex projects may have to obtain a series of approvals, certificates, licenses, permits, land-use rezonings, or variances from local ordinances, depending on the levels of government jurisdiction that apply.

The following section outlines the various stages in the project planning and implementation process where visual simulations can play a key role, including project design, public presentation, environmental assessment, mitigation planning, decision-making, construction, and monitoring.

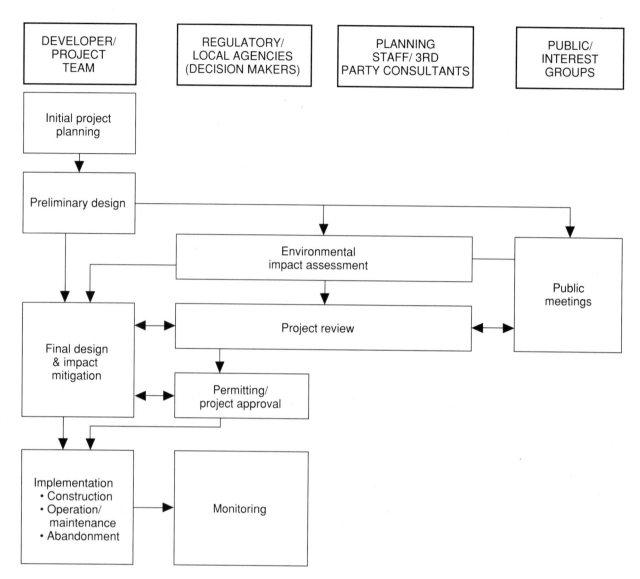

Figure 2-1. Simplified outline of the project planning process.

THE ROLES OF SIMULATION IN PROJECT PLANNING

For each stage of the planning process where simulations could be of benefit, this guide explains

- the advantages of simulation at this stage
- how common it is to use simulations at this stage

- legislative requirements or policies that relate to the use of simulations at this stage

For the purposes of discussing legislative and policy backgrounds regarding simulation, examples are drawn primarily from North America, with some reference to European systems. These two continents contain some of the most advanced planning systems in the world, and currently provide the most comprehensive range of opportunities for simulation use (although the potential is enormous for simulation use as a communications device throughout the world, especially for populations with limited technical capabilities or language barriers).

Project Design and Internal Planning

From the earliest formation of a design idea, visual simulations are relied upon by the designer to record and develop the concept. Sketching on a napkin during lunch is a well-known example (Fig. 2-2). However, the extent to which design proceeds by means of perspective simulations varies.

Many development schemes are designed largely in plan, by mapping out the components of a project or layout. In this instance, simulations are valuable as a check on the evolving design to see if what makes sense in plan also looks right in perspective. This has the following advantages:

- The very act of preparing preliminary simulations such as this may lead the designer to discover unforeseen design complexities that he or she can then resolve. It is not at all uncommon for project designers to be surprised by the appearance of their own creations. This can be avoided by using the simulation process to communicate with one's self, as emphasized by Tommy Wang.[1]
- The principal designer can more fully convey the essence of his or her idea to others on the design team.
- The design can be checked for potential aesthetic problems which, unless dealt with early in the process, could later arouse public opposition or stall agency approval.
- The relative merits of alternative design prototypes can be displayed.

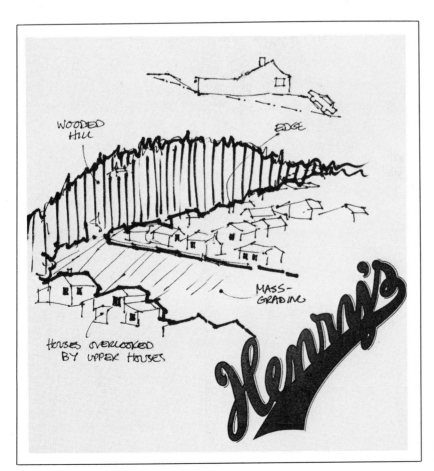

Figure 2-2. "Back-of-a-napkin" conceptual sketches.

Use of simulations in this way is routine in many architecture and landscape architecture firms, but less common in engineering projects.

Where the appearance of the project is likely to be a big issue, the reverse process—*designing in perspective* and converting that information to a plan—may save time and trouble. It is, however, still fairly uncommon as a systematic practice. The advent of computer-aided design and drafting (CADD) systems in architecture and engineering is making the process of designing with perspective simpler to accomplish (Fig. 2-3). Essentially, CADD systems permit designers who lack graphic skills to generate almost instantly a three-dimensional or perspective view of their project from plans and elevations, and even to draw out a project from scratch, directly into the computer. Changes in the design can also be made rapidly and converted from plan/elevation to perspective or, with some systems, from perspective into plans and elevations shown simul-taneously on the same screen. In practice, however, most CADD systems are still being used as drafting machines to produce two-dimensional working drawings, with very limited use as a tool for designing directly in perspective.

General Orientation to the Project

At several stages in the planning process there can be a need for the project to be explained to audiences that are relatively unfamiliar with it. The audience may be the client, project financiers, government staff, special-interest groups, or the general public (Fig. 2-4). Simulations, more than any other kind of communications device, can help such people to grasp the essentials of a project and to visualize it in its entirety. The information that simulations convey may extend far beyond the visual qualities of the project and

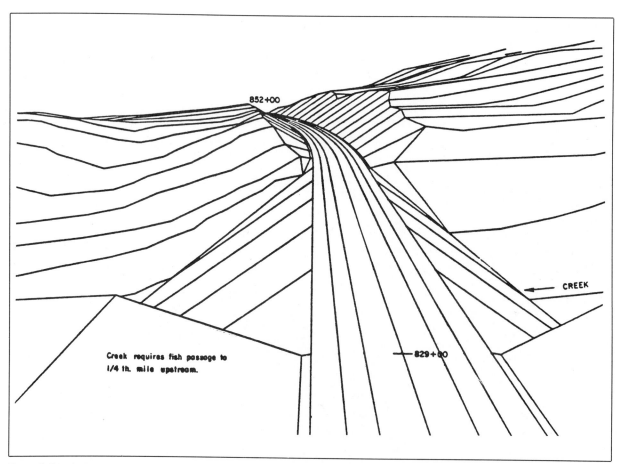

Figure 2-3. CADD simulation used in the design of a highway project.

A new Phoenix rises in downtown Oakland

By Laura Evenson
The Tribune

That hole in the ground on the southwest corner of Eighth and Franklin Streets in downtown Oakland is slated for a $7 million mixed-use commercial/residential condominium project to be completed by August of next year.

Formerly the site of the Galindo Hotel, a swank hostelry built in 1877 and that between 1884 and 1906 was the home of The Tribune, the 21,000-square-foot parcel has been empty since the hotel burned down in 1971.

El Cerrito resident Albert Fong bought the property in 1974 and set up Handsome Properties Inc. in Oakland to develop the site. The new three-story building, to be called Phoenix Plaza, will include 45 condominium units and 15,000 square feet of commercial space.

Handsome, now a subsidiary of Ailanto Properties, said it expects to sell the units for between $140,000 and $170,000 when it begins marketing them in another month.

Del Davis, project manager for the development, said that Handsome Properties hopes to market the development to the community in Oakland's Chinatown because a survey of residents there indicated a strong interest in quality, market-rate housing.

As a result, it plans to include in the retail space food stores from the Chinatown community as well as general merchandise stores and financial institutions. The complex will also include a courtyard designed by Tito Patri, a landscape architect, who is the brother of world-famous Piero Patri. There will also be 56 below-ground parking spaces.

Davis said Fong and his partners decided to name it Phoenix for two reasons. The first is that the phoenix was a mythical, but beautiful, bird that lived for 600 years then consumed itself in fire and rose renewed from the ashes to start another long life. Translation:

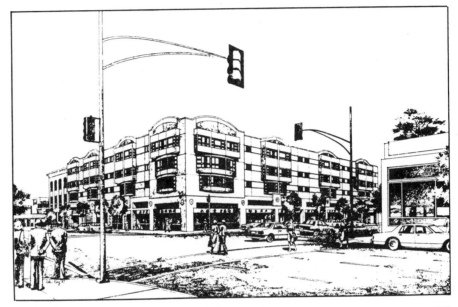

Phoenix Plaza, at 8th and Franklin streets will include 45 condominium units and 15,000 square feet of commercial space.

out City Hall!

CASTOR, SELF BUY MORE BUILDINGS: Oakland investor and developer Ray Castor and his partner, Oakland attorney David Self, have bought two more buildings to their Oakland-based real estate empire. Castor, the majority partner, and Self, who holds a minority interest, bought the buildings from ComputerLand Corp. for $8 million. The two properties at 2901 and 2950 Peralta Oaks Court near the Dunsmuir House, the city-owned Victorian mansion located on Oakland's border with San Leandro. ComputerLand has agreed to continue leasing both buildings, which include a total of 94,362 square feet. Self said that leases will provide cash flow to help pay for financing the purchase. He added that Computerland's lease at 2950 Peralta Oaks Court will expire in 18 months, "so we'll soon be look-

By Frank Pennock/The Tribune

The Galindo Hotel, which once stood on the Phoenix Plaza site, was home to The Tribune in the late 19th and early 20th centuries.

Figure 2-4. Newspaper article using a rendering to display an architectural proposal.

allow the interpreter of the simulation to gain an idea of such things as the scale and duration of the construction activity that will be required, the possible economic effects of the project on the neighborhood, and even the income level of the inhabitants of future residential projects.[2]

The use of simulations as an orientation device has, in fact, been fairly common for a long time. Sir Humphry Repton, the famous landscape architect of eighteenth-century England, used "before" and "after" paintings of his proposed designs to present to clients in his ingenious Red Books (Fig. 2-5 and Plate 2).[3] Many reports on projects today contain illustrations as covers or frontispieces, in recognition of their value as orientation devices. In the author's survey, it was found that approximately 40 percent of all the environmental reports examined contained at least one perspective simulation, and that almost one-third of these were unrelated to any visual assessment.[4] However, in many more cases, requests for additional information on the visual characteristics of projects were made by the public after initial public hearings or distribution of draft reports. This suggests considerable demand for simulations as an information device.

Figure 2-5. Renderings of Antony House by Humphry Repton: existing conditions (with flap in place) *(a);* flap used to show the existing conditions to be altered *(b);* proposed design, revealed by folding back the flap *(c).*

Despite the evident need to orient people to a proposed project, statutory requirements for the use of simulations for this purpose are seldom encountered. It is, however, an expected practice with most design clients, and many planning agencies have ad hoc policies by which requests are made of developers to supply some kind of simulation for purposes of public review (Fig. 2-6).

Environmental Assessment

At the stage where a proposed project needs to be analyzed for its environmental impacts or other consequences, prior to obtaining approval of planning permission from regulatory agencies, simulations can be a very useful analytical tool (Fig. 2-7). They can provide a hard basis for making evaluations, which is advantageous where objective evaluation is critical in conflict situations, or where project alternatives need to be systematically compared.

Simulations can assist project analysis and environmental impact assessment in two ways:

• as *data* which can be analyzed directly by environmental professionals, primarily (but not exclusively) for aesthetic evaluation and visual impact assessment (Fig. 2-8).

Figure 2-6. Simulations depicting alternative types of transmission towers in typical landscape settings. These were specifically requested by the California Energy Commission for inclusion in a public document on the Geothermal Public Power Line Project.

• as a presentation device or controlled *stimulus* to which samples of people can react in surveys to measure attitudes and public responses to the project (Fig. 2-9); in other words, simulations can be used to help generate other data for professional analysis, particularly on public acceptability issues

Figure 2-7   Examples of environmental impact assessments.

The application of these uses of simulation in visual assessment is further discussed in Chapter 3.

Environmental analyses may be conducted at several stages in the planning of a project, particularly with large linear projects such as transportation corridors or long-distance utility lines. Simulations are not common in early analyses for corridor selection or screening of potential project sites, but they may be helpful in clarifying broad visual issues, such as the higher compatibility of a project with one kind of landscape than with another. At later stages in the analysis, when more detailed designs are available, specific project characteristics and locations can be simulated for a finer level of analysis.

A considerable body of legislation exists which indirectly affects simulation use, particularly in the United States. The National Environmental Policy Act (NEPA) of 1969 mandates that aesthetic qualities and other environmental resources be considered and protected in all planning for federal projects and federal land.[5] The California Environmental Quality Act (CEQA)[6] and many other state, county, and city regulations call for similar attention to scenic beauty,

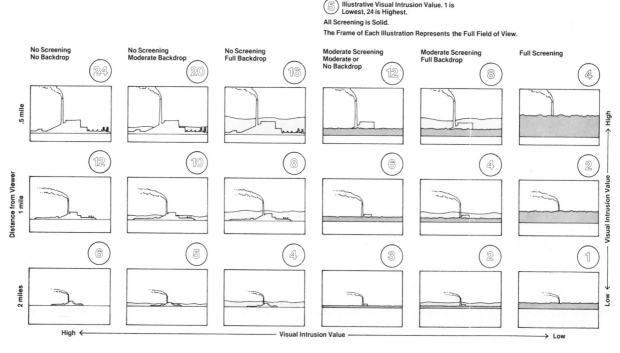

Figure 2-8.   Perspective diagrams used in professional analysis of the visual intrusion of a power plant.

visual impacts, and other environmental concerns within their jurisdictions. Furthermore,
many of these regulations also call for active
public involvement programs by which the opinions of the public and interested parties can be
considered with other data in the analysis.

Figure 2-9.   Model simulations of a proposed highway bridge near Shreveport, Louisi-
ana, as shown to local residents in surveys of public perceptions.

In order to comply with these requirements, environmental and public involvement studies are carried out routinely by project applicants, planning staff, or environmental consultants. However, the regulations seldom stipulate how the aesthetic, environmental, and public-involvement studies should be conducted, and almost never explicitly require the use of visual simulations in the assessment. Consequently, although the use of visual simulations has begun to grow rapidly in this phase of project planning, it is surprising how many aesthetic evaluations and visual impact studies have not employed visual simulations. The author's survey, for example, found that of the visual assessments examined, only 44 percent included perspective simulations, and in many of these cases, the simulations were not directly integrated with the analysis.

It is widely believed by many environmental professionals that they can visualize the appearance and impacts of a project by reading plans sufficiently well to make perspective simulations unnecessary.[7] This places a tremendous reliance upon the abilities of the individual who conducts the visual assessments. Although these beliefs have not been carefully tested, the frequent appearance of unpopular new buildings, for example, suggests that many cases of mistaken judgment do occur.

Mitigation Planning

If an environmental assessment indicates that adverse impacts would result from the project being built, it then becomes important to consider ways in which impacts can be avoided, reduced, or offset. This constitutes *mitigation planning*. Techniques for mitigating impacts normally are derived from the results of the impact assessment itself, by applying design modifications or changes in the construction process to address specific environmental impacts. Visual simulations are again very helpful to environmental professionals both in designing or developing the mitigations, and in assessing their effectiveness or success. Simulations often form both the medium and the catalyst for integrating the impact assessment with the design process. For example, analysis may show that a proposed building would create an unattractive, blank, monumental facade in views from nearby residences; simula-

tions could be prepared to show how much vegetation would be needed to screen the worst parts of the building, as a basis for developing a planting plan to enhance views. Simulations can also explain how biological mitigations, for example, might work, or the visual implications of other mitigations such as noise-barrier construction.

Studies that consider mitigation of project impacts quite frequently use simulations to depict mitigated conditions, although side-by-side comparison with unmitigated conditions are much less common (Fig. 2-10). Requirements for simulations in mitigation planning are, again, very rare.

Documentary Evidence for Agency Decision-making and Court Cases

Once environmental assessment and mitigation planning have taken place, the results of the analysis have to be communicated to the decision-makers in order that they can pass judgment on the project. Simulations are of value here in two ways: in presenting the study findings and recommendations, and in showing how the findings were obtained. Simulations allow the decision-makers to form their own opinion on project impacts and thus verify or check the conclusions reached in the environmental assessment.

The interpreters of simulations at this stage usually include planners, planning commissions, city and county boards or councils, local design review boards, staff of national or state regulatory agencies, and sometimes judges in legal or adjudicatory hearings. In many cases, the public becomes an interpreter whose opinions are weighed in making the final decision. The context in which simulations are presented may be as part of a developer's application package, as illustrations in environmental reports and public documents, as presentations in support of testimony at hearings (Fig. 2-11), or as legal evidence in adversary proceedings. Simulations play a pivotal role in litigation of cases under laws such as the Colorado Supreme Court ruling that scenic views damaged by land condemned for public uses (for example, powerlines) must be compensated for. Under this law, for instance, property owners would be entitled to present any credible evidence on the diminution of market value due to adverse changes in views.

Figure 2-10. Renderings of proposed onshore oil facilities in Santa Barbara County: photograph of preexisting conditions *(a);* simulation of project without mitigation *(b);* simulation with mitigation *(c).*

21

Figure 2-11.   Simulations of Interstate 266 in Arlington, Virginia, presented at public hearings.

In the same way that the substantial body of legislation on aesthetics and environmental quality fails to stipulate that simulations be used in analysis, so it also seldom requires that they be used in project review. An ordinance enacted by Riverside County, California, in 1982, requiring that a simulation accompany all applications to develop wind energy-conversion systems in the county, is a rare and pioneering example (Fig. 2-12 and Plate 3).[8] However, it is often expected by planning boards that some sort of simulation be provided, and informal requests for simulations on a case-by-case basis often are made, although the type of simulation seldom is specified.

Guides for Construction

It is quite possible for visual simulations to be used in the same way as plans or design specifications—to guide the project construction process (Fig. 2-13). For example, the construction manager may attempt to position boulders in a rock garden as they are shown in a design sketch, or to match the colors of a painted sur-

Figure 2-12.   Simulation required for a proposed wind-turbine development in San Gorgonio Pass, Riverside County, California.

face to those shown in a simulation. This allows a particular design effect that is difficult to describe in normal specifications, plans, or working drawings to be conveyed accurately to the builder. It can be valuable in two main situations:

• with projects using materials and layouts that are not standard and where the builder would otherwise have considerable leeway in arranging or selecting items, especially where

the precise dimensions of the material cannot be predicted before arrival on-site
- where the design exists in a perspective simulation only or where plan and nonperspective design drawings cannot be fully trusted as correct

Documented examples of simulations used in this manner are rare and generally confined to placement of natural landscape elements in high-quality design projects where aesthetic details are accorded major importance (Fig. 2-14).

It would be quite feasible for permitting agencies to include, as part of the permit conditions, the requirement that certain simulations be used during construction to help create in reality the desired visual effect. Again, however, documented instances of such recommendations or requirements are hard to find.

Figure 2-13. Construction site.

a

b

Figure 2-14. Recreation facilities at Incline Village, Nevada. Similarities between the drawing *(a)* prepared at the design stage and the actual site as built *(b)* suggest that construction was guided by the simulation.

Postconstruction Evaluation and Monitoring

Once a project is built, simulations may be used as a visual baseline or standard against which the actual performance of the project can be measured. This is particularly useful in questions of long-term compliance with stipulated or expected conditions; for example, it would be possible to monitor the time taken for vegetation to grow until it screened the project to the extent shown in the original simulations (Fig. 2-15 and Plate 4).

To the author's knowledge, such use of simulations has rarely been formally implemented. It is most likely to occur in land management agencies such as the U.S. Forest Service, where simulations often are used to help plan long-term management activities (such as timber harvesting) that affect visual qualities. At Beaver Creek, Colorado, time-lapse photography of the clearing of ski runs on forest land has enabled Forest Service staff to compare actual results with predictive simulations (Fig. 2-16 and Plate 5).[9]

As a spin-off benefit, postconstruction evaluation of project appearance also permits evaluation of the performance of simulations in terms of their ability to predict the actual appearance of the project (see Fig. 2-16a, d). In fact, this reason may account for more postconstruction monitoring than may a direct interest in project

Figure 2-15. Computer graphics which model the expected growth of landscaping established to mitigate powerline impacts.

performance. Agencies that use visual simulations frequently, such as Bonneville Power Administration, Montana Power Company, and Electricité de France, are beginning to conduct postconstruction monitoring for this purpose. Some of the better professional illustrators record the postconstruction views, in part as an effective marketing device for their renderings (Fig. 2-17). Surprisingly, however, there are very few systematic examples of such monitoring.[4,10] To date, the author is not aware of any such monitoring required or formalized in policy by a permitting agency.

Other Roles for Visual Simulation

Visual simulation has several applications that can indirectly but significantly influence the project planning process.

PREDICTION OF NATURAL OR LONG-TERM ENVIRONMENTAL CHANGE. Although most simulations in practice are closely associated with a particular project, they can also be used to show environmental change where man takes *no* action.

a

b

c

d

Figure 2-16. Time-lapse photography used to monitor progress of ski run development at Beaver Creek, Colorado: perspective plot simulation of proposed ski runs *(a)*; same view before development (August 1975) *(b)*; view after development (September 1979) *(c)*; view after further development (February 1981) *(d)*.

Figure 2-17.   Comparison of a rendering *(a)* of the proposed Portland Museum of Art, Portland, Maine, with a photograph *(b)* of the same view four years later.

All landscapes are continually undergoing natural change, notably by *vegetative succession.* This is where certain plant species replace earlier pioneering species and are themselves succeeded by others as plant growth changes site conditions. Anyone who has compared photographs of their house and garden as they were fifteen years ago with their appearance now will know how much a landscape can change due to tree growth, death of plants, aging of structures, and invasion by new plants. If we were to sit back and do nothing for the next ten years, most if not all of the landscapes that have been modified by man would change considerably.

This may be of passing interest to most people, although simulations would help gardeners and park managers, for instance, to plan how to maintain, control, or remove trees that would otherwise eventually block views or shade out other plants. In some situations, however, this kind of information can be crucial in land management. At Yosemite National Park, for example, vegetation succession without control by prescribed burning would gradually eliminate the open meadows that contribute so much to the park's scenic image and permit open views to its other features. A similar situation exists on the Blue Ridge Parkway, North Carolina (Fig. 2-18 and Plate 6).[11]

In fact, the "do-nothing" approach is actually just an alternative management treatment that will result in specific landscape changes. Like any other project, its effects can be analyzed and simulated. Environmental impact assessments normally require analysis of the *no-project*

alternative, which is often taken to be the status quo. However, it actually takes an intensive management effort to preserve existing landscape conditions. In assessment of a long-term project or one slated for construction many years hence, the no-project alternative with which it should be compared, in visual terms, is not the existing landscape at the time of the analysis, but the expected future landscape, assuming natural or typical landscape change. Visual simulations are the principal means of indicating such conditions, although this usage virtually never occurs and has never been required by a government agency, to the author's knowledge.

Other long-term environmental changes may result from natural catastrophes such as volcanic eruptions and earthquakes, or from man's influence as a result not of specific projects but of cumulative actions. For example, desertification by overgrazing, forest damage by acid rain, and buildup of air pollution[12] can all be brought into stark focus by simulations that telescope gradual change into a before-and-after comparison. Simulation techniques have been applied in this context for both mass-media consumption and scientific research.

ENVIRONMENTAL AND PERCEPTUAL RESEARCH. Simulations are used as stimuli with which to obtain people's responses to proposed environments for purposes of academic research. This use is very similar to the applied studies used in visual assessments to obtain expert or community responses to project alternatives. The results are used to test general theories of how people perceive landscapes and project types.[13] The findings can be applied to project-specific studies with similar conditions, and be used to predict or substitute for actual responses where these would be difficult to obtain. The advantage of visual simulations is that they can be designed to control a number of visual variables of interest for purposes of statistical analysis (Fig. 2-19). For example, if researchers were testing for the effects of color on the attractiveness of pedestrian footbridges as judged by engineering students, they could standardize the types of bridges, lighting conditions, and surroundings by using the same pictures and changing only the bridge colors by simulation. Any differences in students' responses would thus be due to the colors of the bridge and not to extraneous differences in the scenes shown.

a

b

Figure 2-18. Vegetative management alternatives for the Blue Ridge Parkway, North Carolina: photosimulation of views with mowing and cutting *(a)*; photograph showing effects of natural growth on scenic views *(b)*.

a

b

Figure 2-19. Simulations used by the author to test people's reactions to controlled amounts of detail in pictures of a housing project in Marin County, California: minimal detail *(a)*; intermediate level of detail *(b)*; more complete detail *(c)*.

c

Simulations have been used in this way in environmental and perceptual research,[14,15] although it has been far more common to test reactions to existing views (photographs) in an attempt to understand which characteristics of landscapes make them more or less beautiful to people. Controlled tests using properly prepared simulations provide a much more powerful and direct approach to answering this kind of question by analyzing cause and effect rather than looking for patterns of response with uncontrolled actual scenes.

ENVIRONMENTAL TRAINING. Designers, planners, and others who intend to become involved in landscape issues and project planning benefit from using simulations to evaluate their own plans and designs during training. Simulations can be a major learning tool, aiding students to see and treat problems in their own designs and, in some cases, to improve their skills in visualizing projects without simulations. Such use in training also demonstrates some of the advantages and potential drawbacks of simulations.

Some form of perspective simulation usually is required in course work for architects and landscape architects. It is seldom taught, however, beyond the level of rendering and sketching techniques or of simple computer graphics, and the emphasis often is laid upon attractive graphics — in other words, the medium and not the real message. Engineering students, planning students, and professionals or lay people involved in planning commissions or city councils very seldom receive any training at all in the use of simulations.

Summary

Throughout the typical planning process (especially the stages from project design through documentary evidence for decision-making, described above), simulations can provide important visual information obtainable by no other means. In particular, they provide opportunities for illuminating comparisons and clearer communication, as follows:

- Side-by-side comparison of existing and future conditions (Fig. 2-20 and Plate 7)
- Side-by-side comparison of alternative project designs (Fig. 2-21)
- Side-by-side comparison of future conditions at different points in time (Fig. 2-22); for example, reclamation of disturbed land can be simulated at different stages—from conditions during active project operations, one year after initial reseeding, and ten years after reseeding—showing successful reestablishment of vegetation
- Side-by-side comparison of different views of the same proposed project (Fig. 2-23)
- Visualizing unusual or unfamiliar technologies, such as wind-turbine facilities, new rapid-transit systems, and new communications installations (Fig. 2-24)
- Providing a common basis of understanding (a universal language) for environmental professionals of different disciplines, and for people with different levels of expertise, from expert to layman

_a_

_b_

Figure 2-20. Photograph of existing conditions *(a)* along Interstate 25 in Denver, Colorado, and a photosimulation *(b)* of proposed busways.

Figure 2-21. Three renderings of alternative designs for a power plant.

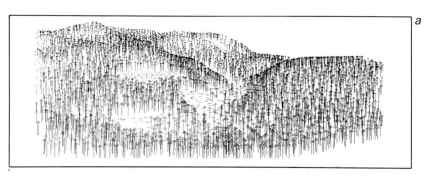

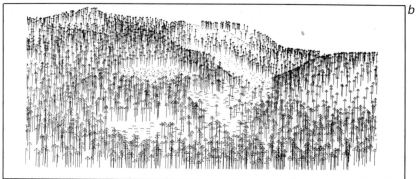

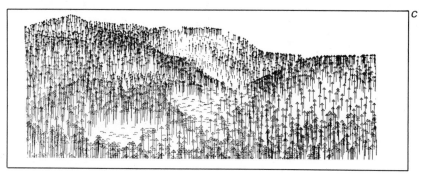

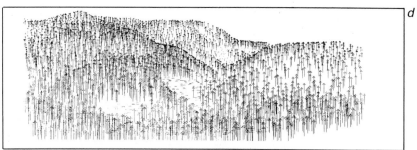

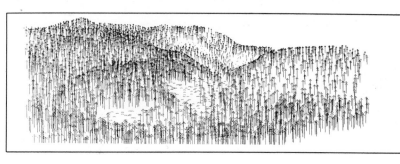

Figure 2-22. Simulations of 152 years of timber harvesting on the Boulder Sale Area, Gifford Pinchot National Forest, generated by the PREVIEW program: year 1 before commercial harvesting *(a)*; year 1 after initial cutting *(b)*; year 39, after second cut *(c)*; year 115, after several further cutting cycles *(d)*; year 153, after continued cutting *(e)*.

Figure 2-23. Photosimulations of different views of the same proposed electrical substation in Billings, Montana.

a

b

Figure 2-24.   Proposed telecommunications facilities site: photograph of preexisting site *(a);* photosimulation of proposed facilities *(b).*

BENEFITS OF SIMULATION USE IN PROJECT PLANNING

If simulations were used in a way that fulfilled their potential as described in this chapter, what would be the likely result? How would the course of project planning be affected if good simulations were used, as opposed to poor simulations or none at all? What difference would it make to the fate of the project and to the interests of developers, agencies, and the public?

In considering these questions, the most crucial stage in the process is that of governmental project review and approval. This is where decisions can be made to deny a project or completely alter its nature. There are definitely situations in which simulations can make or break a project. The process as commonly conducted by review agencies, together with possible outcomes of using or not using good simulations, is illustrated in Figure 2-25.

On the one hand, there are, without doubt, instances of inappropriate projects being ap-

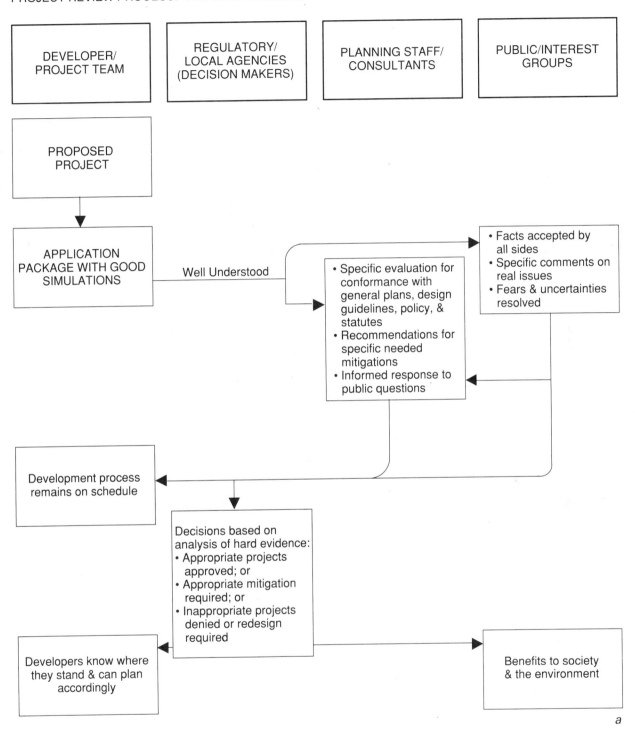

Figure 2-25. The project-review process: with good simulations *(a)*; without good simulations *(b,* next page).

PROJECT REVIEW PROCESS: Without Good Simulations

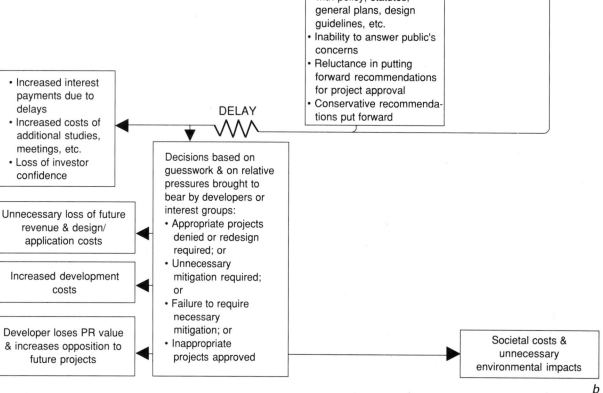

DEVELOPER/ PROJECT TEAM

REGULATORY/ LOCAL AGENCIES (DECISION MAKERS)

PLANNING STAFF/ CONSULTANTS

PUBLIC/ INTEREST GROUPS

PROPOSED PROJECT

APPLICATION PACKAGE WITH NO SIMULATIONS OR POOR SIMULATIONS

Poorly Understood

• Uncertainty
• Conflicting interpretations
• Unfocused controversy
• Opportunities provided for opposition to project
• Fears magnified
• Requests for further studies & information

• Reliance on guesswork & visualizing skills
• Uncertainty on conformity with policy, statutes, general plans, design guidelines, etc.
• Inability to answer public's concerns
• Reluctance in putting forward recommendations for project approval
• Conservative recommendations put forward

• Increased interest payments due to delays
• Increased costs of additional studies, meetings, etc.
• Loss of investor confidence

DELAY

Decisions based on guesswork & on relative pressures brought to bear by developers or interest groups:
• Appropriate projects denied or redesign required; or
• Unnecessary mitigation required; or
• Failure to require necessary mitigation; or
• Inappropriate projects approved

Unnecessary loss of future revenue & design/ application costs

Increased development costs

Developer loses PR value & increases opposition to future projects

Societal costs & unnecessary environmental impacts

b

Figure 2-25. *(continued)*.

36

proved and built when they might have been stopped altogether or (more commonly) redesigned, had good simulations been used. A developer taking the short-term view might find it beneficial to avoid good simulations in such instances. However, the negative reactions to the built project may damage its and the developer's public image and make approval of future proposals harder or more expensive to achieve, both for that developer and for others proposing similar projects (Fig. 2-26). In an age when public concern over environmental quality and social impacts is steadily growing, the approval of inappropriate projects can no longer be excused. Given the abundance of sophisticated simulation techniques available today, it is strange that the construction of buildings and facilities that are generally perceived as eyesores is still so common. As the president of the Municipal Art Society of New York said in reference to proposed high-rises in Manhattan's theater district: ''The public ought to ask to see simulations in every major land-use decision. Then you won't hear people commenting, 'How did the city ever let that happen.'''[16]

On the other hand, it is common for private developers, utility companies, and other bodies responsible for the construction of projects to feel that their schemes have been unjustly turned down or the design needlessly constrained on the basis of vague opinions, exaggerated fears, blanket regulations, or the influence of persuasive special-interest groups.

Given the make-or-break significance of people's perceptions in project approval, it would be of benefit to all concerned to obtain and communicate good information and understanding of the project. Visual simulations can be one of the best means to achieve this. In the author's experience, it is common for the public's perception of a proposed project to be worse than its actual response to either the built project or a good simulation of it. Good simulations can do much to bring people toward a consensus on the project and allow them to focus on real issues, eliminating time-wasting debate on whether the information they have to evaluate is adequate or correct.

For many projects, it is difficult to predict with certainty the outcome of the project-review process. Therefore, the risk of uncertainty, delay, and opposition to a project must always concern project proponents and developers. Indeed, the very risk of a negative decision, based on poor information or the lack of hard evidence with which to refute biased accusations, makes it in the developer's interest to use good visual simulations. They can, therefore, be viewed as an insurance policy. If the simulations indicate no unforeseen problems with the project, the developer's position is strengthened. If the simulations reveal real problems with the project, then these can be dealt with early; if the developer decides not to modify the project and project approval is denied, he cannot claim that he has been unjustly penalized. Any developer who attempts to gain project approval by suppressing or distorting information of the type that good simulations would convey is knowingly assuming a strong risk of failure wherever vigorous agency or public scrutiny is applied. In fact, if it can be demonstrated that a thorough analysis of the project has been undertaken and that potential problems have been eliminated or reduced through redesign aided by simulations, the prospects for project approval in environmentally sensitive situations can be greatly enhanced. Even where problems remain, full disclosure may make decision-makers more ready to accept them; a good adage for simulation preparers could well be, ''People will be realistic if you are.''

Lastly, where simulations are used as an insurance policy for developers, they are remarkably inexpensive in relation to their potential value. The cost of even a sophisticated series of simulations is negligible compared with total design costs, public-relations budgets, projected revenues, or losses resulting from denial or unnecessary redesign of a project. It is doubtful whether simulation costs ever approach even 1 percent of the total costs of designing and constructing a project.

Figure 2-26. San Francisco's Embarcadero Freeway, which blocked off views to the Bay from the city, caused a storm of protest, and may be pulled down; better use of simulations might have avoided these problems and the enormous expense involved.

The advantages of using good simulations at the project-review stage of project planning also apply to other stages in the process. In fact, the earlier in the process that simulations are used to screen and eliminate design problems, the better the chances for a streamlined process and rapid approval of appropriate projects. Likewise, simulations used for guiding construction and for postconstruction monitoring can help to ensure that construction is not halted due to unforeseen project characteristics, and that planned mitigations do not turn out to be false promises or frills to be dispensed with once approval has been granted.

REFERENCES

1. Wang, T. 1986. Personal communication.

2. Appleyard, D. 1976. "Environmental simulation in planning and design." Unpublished paper, Dept. of Landscape Architecture, University of California, Berkeley.

3. Malins, E. 1976. *The Red Books of Humphry Repton.* Vol. IV, London: Basilisk Press.

4. Sheppard, S. R. J. 1982. "Landscape portrayals: their use, accuracy, and validity in simulating proposed landscape changes." Ph.D. diss. University of California, Berkeley.

5. National Environmental Policy Act of 1969. Debate on Conf. Report No. 765, *Cong. Rec.,* 91st Congress, 1st Session, 1969, 115, 40415-27.

6. California Environmental Quality Act of 1970. Cal. Pub. Res. Code #21000.

7. Shuttleworth, S. 1984. Personal communication.

8. Riverside County, California. 1982. Land Use Ordinance 348, Article XVIII, Section 18-41. p. 221.

9. U.S. Forest Service. 1984. *National Forest Landscape Management,* Vol. 2, Chap. 7, Ski Areas. Agriculture Handbook No. 617. Washington, D.C.: U.S. Dept. of Agriculture.

10. Wood, W. 1972. "An analysis of simulation media." Master's thesis, University of British Columbia, Vancouver.

11. Day, T. R. 1987. "Simulating vegetative management techniques utilizing color photographic montage." Paper presented at the "Aesthetics of the Rural Renaissance" Conference, San Luis Obispo, Calif., August 27–29.

12. Treiman, E. F., D. B. Champion, M. J. Wecksung, G. H. Moore, A. Ford, and M. D. Williams. 1979. "Simulation of the visual effects of power plant plumes." In *Our National Landscape,* Conference Proceedings, ed. G. H. Elsner and R. C. Smardon, U.S. Dept. of Agriculture Forest Service, General Technical Report PSW-35. Berkeley, Calif.: Pacific Southwest Forest and Range Experiment Station.

13. Wohlwill, J. F. 1978. "What belongs where?—Research on fittingness of man-made structures in natural settings." *Landscape Research* 3(3):3–5.

14. Craik, K. H., D. Appleyard, and G. E. McKechnie. 1980. *Impressions of a Place: Effects of Media and Familiarity among Environmental Professionals.* Research Technical Report. Berkeley, Calif.: Institute of Personality Assessment and Research, University of California.

15. Danford, S., and E. P. Williams. 1975. "Subjective responses to architectural displays: a question of validity." *Environment and Behavior* 7:486–516.

16. Barwick, K. 1986. Quoted in "Visual simulations gain as planning aids," *Wall Street Journal.* July 9, p. 25.

Chapter **3**

THE ROLE OF SIMULATION
IN VISUAL ANALYSIS

Visual analysis or *visual resource assessment* is the study of the appearance or visual qualities of environments and proposed environmental changes. Its purpose is to identify existing landscape values and resources, determine how these would be changed by new projects, and suggest ways to conserve or enhance these values and resources where appropriate. Visual analysis can be applied to projects in urban, rural, or natural environments. Since visual analysis provides the context in which many simulations are used in practice, it is important to understand the concepts and process of which it consists. Furthermore, simulations are most effective when integrated into the visual analysis process, rather than being prepared as illustrations after the analysis is complete.

Visual resource assessment was recognized as a major environmental discipline in the United States with the enactment of the National Environmental Policy Act (NEPA) in 1969. This required that aesthetics be considered as a resource equal in value to other natural resources, such as wildlife and air quality, in the environmental impact assessment of all major federal actions. The NEPA itself, however, was in part a response to public concern for aesthetics which

had been felt increasingly in North America and Europe in the preceding years, and also to early pioneering studies on aesthetics and landscape management.[1] People had begun to complain, for example, about the ugliness of billboards along highways (Fig. 3-1) and the scars of clear-cutting in national forests. Government agencies were spurred into action to find solutions to visual problems.

The methods of visual analysis adopted by the largest land management agencies in the

Figure 3-1. The visual blight of billboards, as shown here, demonstrated the need for policies to protect landscape quality.

U.S. to respond to this need have been the best known and most widely applied.[2,3] They lend themselves, first and foremost, to the planning and management of large areas with relatively natural landscapes. Generally, they need to be adapted for the purposes of visual impact assessment of proposed projects. Many other agencies, researchers, and private companies involved with visual analysis have developed or adapted methods of assessment and there is considerable literature available (see references in the Bibliography under Visual Analysis and Perception). Current efforts on developing methodologies appear to be focusing more and more on the issues of appropriate urban design and the importance of cultural associations and perceived meanings in rural and urban landscapes.

Visual analysis has two major components:

1. Analysis of the landscape itself, including elements of the physical landscape and the manner in which it is viewed by people. This kind of analysis should be carried out by trained landscape professionals.

2. Analysis of people's responses to the landscape; for example, how much they like a particular view. The people may be a panel of trained observers, or, more commonly, various representatives of the major interest groups concerned with the project, such as local residents, land management agencies, landowners, and recreation groups.

Although some approaches to visual analysis rely solely upon professional evaluation of landscapes, and others exclusively upon observers' responses, it is possible and increasingly common for both components to be incorporated. Visual simulations are of value with most if not all approaches. There follows a brief outline of a general procedure into which simulations fit. The procedure is consistent with NEPA requirements for inventory and impact assessment in the United States, but is applicable to the visual analysis of any project. Principles and criteria that are relevant to simulation use are emphasized.

GENERALIZED PROCESS FOR PROJECT VISUAL ANALYSIS

The visual analysis process may be divided into four principal phases: inventory, impact assessment, mitigation, and monitoring.

Visual Inventory

This involves description and evaluation of existing landscapes, sites, or built projects in terms of a number of aspects, as shown in Figure 3-2. These aspects include:

OVERALL VISUAL CHARACTER.   Patterns of landform, vegetation, water, land use, and structures (Fig. 3-3).

SCENIC OR VISUAL QUALITY.   The attractiveness or distinctiveness of the landscape, site, or built projects (Fig. 3-4 and Plate 8).

VIEWING CONDITIONS.   The viewpoints from which the landscape, site, or project is seen, the distance and viewshed (visible area) over which it is seen (Fig. 3-5 and Plate 9), and typical lighting and visibility conditions (Fig. 3-6 and Plate 10).

VIEWER CHARACTERISTICS.   Numbers of viewers, frequency and duration of viewing, and type of activity in which the viewer is taking part (for example, recreating at a particular location versus driving to or from work).

VIEWER SENSITIVITY.   The degree of concern that viewers have for existing visual qualities (for example, how much they care about a local mountain view or open space).

VISUAL POLICIES.   Regulations or guidelines affecting visual resources, enacted by government agencies with responsibilities for land management and planning. Examples that can apply to a project site might include scenic highway designations, wilderness area management policies, design review guidelines, and conservation area stipulations.

These landscape attributes can be analyzed by field survey, inspection of maps, documents and site photographs, and interviews with local residents and agency staff. However, there are further attributes which often are analyzed as part of the inventory in studies directed toward the siting of particular projects. Here the need is to establish where the better (more compatible) and worse (more constrained) locations are for a project from a visual standpoint. Such analyses address the following aspects.

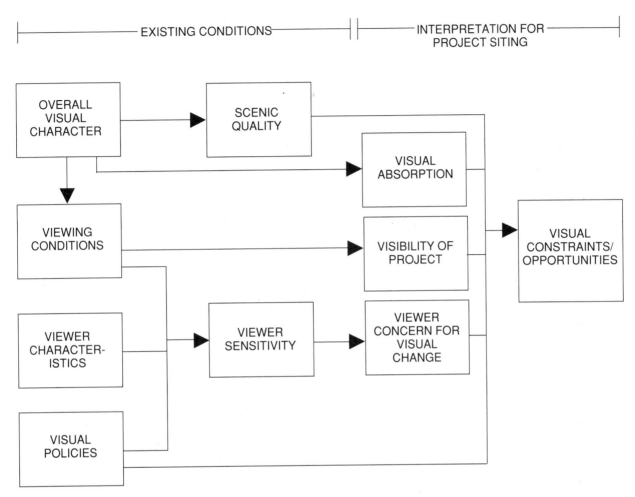

Figure 3-2.   Conceptual process for visual inventory.

Figure 3-3. Landscape with dominant landforms and a mixture of water and vegetative features, structures, and other man-made elements.

41

a

b

Figure 3-4. Scenic quality: relatively high where diverse landscape elements fit together harmoniously in a distinctive landscape *(a)*; relatively low where landscape is monotonous and undistinctive *(b)*.

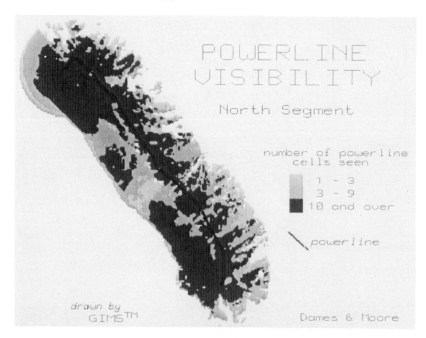

Figure 3-5. Viewshed map, showing the area of land from which a powerline would be visible, with different viewing frequencies.

a

b

Figure 3-6. Views of the same object seen in different directions with different lighting conditions: frontlighting (viewing the illuminated side) *(a)*; backlighting (viewing the shaded side) *(b)*.

VISUAL ABSORPTION. The degree to which landscape modifications or projects could be absorbed into existing landscape patterns without noticeably affecting scenic quality (Fig. 3-7).[4] For instance, a landscape with a mixture of rolling fields, woods, and farm buildings would absorb the visual impact of a new farm building much more readily than would a flat, open landscape with no trees or other buildings.

VIEWER CONCERN FOR VISUAL CHANGE. The degree to which people care about the prospect of visual change by particular types of project. For instance, local people may be more concerned about the appearance of a proposed transmission line crossing nearby open land than about the appearance of a proposed housing development in the same vicinity. Inevitably, these kinds of comparisons and evaluations will involve more than purely visual concerns. For example, land values and individual attitudes toward development may influence people's feelings, but the visual impact serves to focus and symbolize people's overall concerns.

VISIBILITY OF STRUCTURES. Assuming a given height for a certain type of project, it is possible by line-of-sight calculations or computer analysis

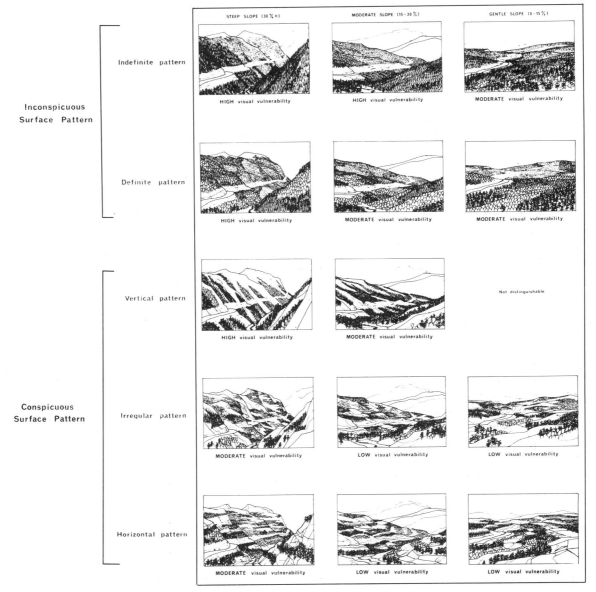

Figure 3-7. Visual absorption or visual vulnerability of the landscape, determined by slope and surface patterns.

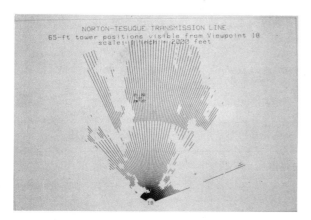

Figure 3-8. Viewshed map showing, on an overlay to a topographic map, those areas in which a 65-foot tower would be seen from a given viewpoint.

Figure 3-9. Two alternative simulations shown to residents of an Arizona community as part of an attempt to discover their preferences for different transmission-line configurations.

to map out a modified viewshed showing all possible locations in which at least part of such a structure would be seen from particular viewpoints (Fig. 3-8).

VISUAL CONSTRAINTS AND OPPORTUNITIES. The extent to which a certain type of project would potentially be compatible with different areas in the landscape, taking into account all of the above considerations.

Some of these types of analysis can benefit from the use of simulations. In order to evaluate how well a range of landscapes would absorb a particular kind of project, there is a need to visualize how noticeable the project would be in the various settings. This could be assessed on the basis of a professional's experience from earlier studies, photographs of a range of similar situations elsewhere, or simulations of typical situations (see Chapter 5 for more detailed discussion of generic simulations).

Similarly, information on people's concerns can be obtained from reactions to photographs of similar situations elsewhere, or from simulations of typical situations (Fig. 3-9). It is often of value to find out how concerns differ with a particular kind of project in different situations. For example, a proposed structure can elicit more or less concern depending upon how far away from the viewer it would be, whether it would be seen against the sky rather than against a backdrop of hills, and whether it is brightly colored rather than subdued in color. This kind of information can help both in planning to locate projects in less sensitive areas, and in developing criteria for assessing visual impacts and specific

project proposals later. In these cases, it is often simpler to control the variables being tested—for instance, distance or color—by means of simulations, rather than to obtain a large number of actual photographs to show what is required. Simulations usually are shown to the observers in a workshop where participants enter their responses in questionnaires, or in mail surveys where simulations are reproduced and sent to participants with mail-back questionnaires.

Visual Impact Assessment

Once the location and general design of a proposed project have been determined (including any project alternatives), the project can be analyzed in more detail in terms of its effects on visual resources (Fig. 3-10). Here simulations are of major importance.

The process of evaluating visual impacts includes some or all of the following aspects.

PROJECT DESCRIPTION. This specifies those physical aspects of a project that would affect its appearance, such as surface materials, type of landscaping, paint colors, and reflectivity of glass. Some of this information can be presented in nonperspective simulations such as elevations and working drawings, or in perspective simulations showing close views of the project.

VISUAL PROMINENCE. This is the degree to which a project would be noticeable or prominent in relation to its setting, in general or particular views. Visual prominence, also known as *visual contrast*[3] and *visual dominance,*[5] can range from none (where a project cannot be seen or distinguished), to high (where it dominates the entire view and draws nearly all of the viewer's attention). It should not automatically be assumed that high prominence is bad (see below). The level of visual prominence of a project or other landscape feature is influenced by a number of factors or visual elements, as shown in Figure 3-11 and Plate 11.[5]

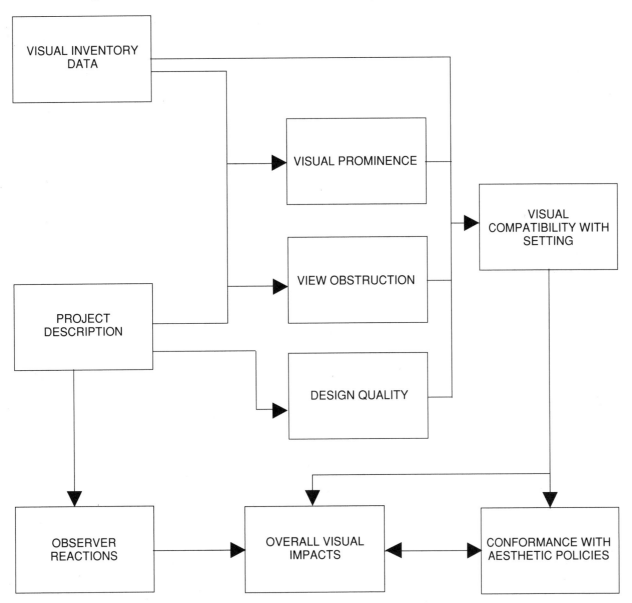

Figure 3-10. Conceptual process for visual impact assessment.

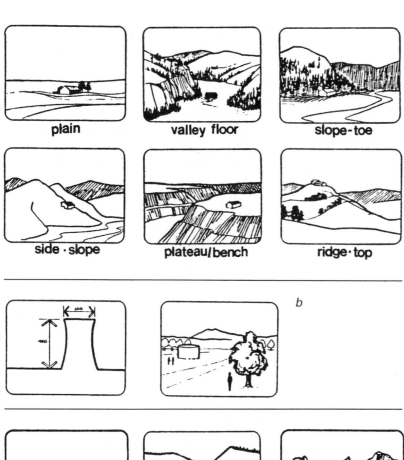

a

plain   valley floor   slope-toe

side·slope   plateau/bench   ridge·top

Spatial position *(a)* of the project in relation to the three-dimensional arrangement of objects and voids in the landscape. Important spatial aspects of the project include relationship to the skyline, location in topographic spaces such as focal valleys or broad plains, and position with regard to streetscapes and architectural arrangements.

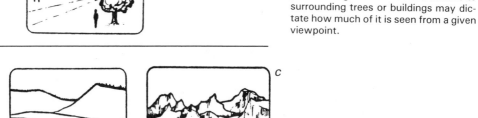

b

Scale *(b)*—the apparent size of a project in relation to its surroundings. For example, the height of a structure relative to surrounding trees or buildings may dictate how much of it is seen from a given viewpoint.

c

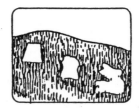

Shape or form *(c)*—the configuration and outline of the project in terms of masses, patterns, and linear elements. For example, a structure may have a bulky, vertical, geometric silhouette which contrasts with an irregular horizontal landscape of rolling hills.

d

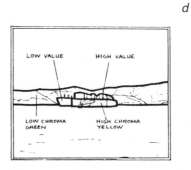

LOW VALUE   HIGH VALUE

LOW CHROMA GREEN   HIGH CHROMA YELLOW

Color *(d)*—the light-reflecting qualities of a project's surface (for example, dark or light, blue or gray) in relation to background colors.

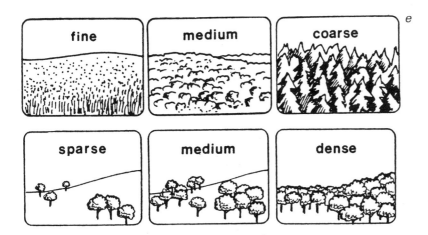

e

Texture and detail *(e)*—details of surface pattern, as in smooth polished metal surfaces versus the rough, uneven textures of the foliage of trees and bushes.

Figure 3-11. Factors affecting visual prominence of a project.

Spatial position, scale, and shape or form may be thought of as primarily *structural elements,* expressing mainly three-dimensional qualities. Color, line, and texture and detail, on the other hand, are primarily *surface elements,* expressing mainly two-dimensional qualities. All of these visual elements are affected by other variable conditions such as viewing distance, the direction from which the project would be seen, or lighting conditions. It is possible for these elements and conditions to be visualized mentally by experienced observers, and in some cases to be calculated by other means (as in drawing cross sections to discover how much of a project may be seen above lower intervening objects, or computing the visual magnitude of objects in the field-of-view[6]). By far the most helpful tool in analyzing visual prominence, nonetheless, is a visual simulation in which visual elements and relationships between objects are shown explicitly.

VIEW OBSTRUCTION.   This is the degree to which the project would permit or block views toward existing landscape features. For example, a building may block the views of local residents toward

distant mountains, or their views of a scrap yard. Conversely, a project may, by removing trees, expose a view of mountains or a scrap yard. Regardless of the merits of view obstruction or exposure, its extent in particular views is best shown in simulations, which can indicate precisely those parts of the landscape that would be affected (Fig. 3-12). Without simulations of moving views, maps form the best method of showing the geographic extent of view obstruction (for example, the length of highway affected).

DESIGN QUALITY. Design quality describes the aesthetic characteristics of the project design itself, normally as determined by professionals using criteria such as distinctiveness and visual harmony of the design components. For example, a carefully planned recreational lake may be as visually prominent as a mine-site tailings pond, but could be significantly more attractive. Similarly, two buildings may be equally visible, but one may have a more appealing design. Simulations form a better basis for judging visual design quality than do plans and specifications.

Figure 3-12. Simulation showing extent of view blockage by a proposed office building.

LANDMARK STATUS AND ORIENTATION. These characteristics describe the ability of a project to symbolize important site or community values, and to provide geographic orientation to visitors and people. Examples of projects that fulfill this function include the Seattle Space Needle and San Francisco's Transamerica pyramid. Good simulations are the best way to determine whether the proposed landmark is visually dominant enough to orient viewers, and whether it establishes an appropriate image for the location.

VISUAL COMPATIBILITY. This is the degree to which the project would actually be compatible with the visual qualities of its setting, taking into account the professional evaluations of location and design described above.

OBSERVERS' REACTIONS. *Preferences* indicate the observers' relative like or dislike of project components, project alternatives, and no-project scenarios. As with the more general responses on concern for visual change discussed above, other nonvisual factors will influence how particular people may react. *Judgments* of specific visual characteristics of project alternatives (in questions such as, "How much would this project change the appearance of the landscape?") tend to be more consistent between different observers than do general questions of preference.[7,8] Both methods, though uncommonly carried out in practice, can provide useful (if different) information; both require visual simulations if reasonable reliability of responses is to be obtained, particularly where untrained observers are being used.[9]

Research has shown that people's preferences for scenes are influenced by the verbal description or title, as well as by the visual content of the scene itself; for example, people seem to prefer scenes labeled "natural forest" over identical scenes labeled "managed timber stand."[10] In this light, simulations can be helpful in separating the visual responses to proposed projects from other responses related to factors such as safety and land values. A set of simulations showing different project types or alternatives in the same setting, without accompanying value-laden descriptions, can provide objective data on the visual impacts of, for example, a nuclear power plant as compared to a coal-fired power plant or factory.

OVERALL VISUAL IMPACTS. By integrating the project-specific analyses with relevant general information from the visual inventory (for example, scenic quality and viewing conditions), levels of visual impact are assigned to project components and alternatives. Impacts can be expressed in terms of type (for example, reduction in scenic qualities, or effects on highway views); direction (adverse versus beneficial); duration (short-term to permanent); and level (high to low). This information typically is combined with results of studies on other environmental issues, leading to an overall assessment or ranking of project alternatives. Simulations can help in a general way to support and illustrate the assessment results.

CONFORMANCE WITH VISUAL POLICIES. Visual impacts need to be interpreted as to their conformance or nonconformance with agency policies and regulations governing visual resources and project design. Again, simulations can help to explain how well a project conforms to requirements, both technically and in spirit.

Visual Mitigation

Once visual impacts have been described, ways of mitigating or reducing adverse impacts are considered. This usually begins with a listing of possible project treatments to address particular visual problems; for example, high visual impacts due to cut-and-fill slopes of a proposed road along a steep hillside may be mitigated by realigning the road along the flatter valley bottom, or by reestablishing vegetation on the exposed cut-and-fill slopes.

Those visual mitigations that are feasible are then reanalyzed (as described in the preceding section on Visual Impact Assessment) for their effectiveness in reducing visual impacts, and final residual impacts are determined for the project with mitigation.

Simulations can be helpful in

- identifying the exact causes and extent of particular visual problems, as simulated for the unmitigated project
- designing various mitigation treatments: for example, by sketching out modified road alignments or testing the advantages of grouping similar structures together in clusters (Fig. 3-13)

- assessing the residual visual impacts of the project, as simulated with selected mitigation treatments

Monitoring Visual Impacts

No standard procedures for monitoring visual impacts over time have been established, although Litton has suggested an approach based on a network of viewpoints or "landscape control points."[11] In general, monitoring requires an evaluation of actual visual impacts and comparison with predicted visual impacts. It is, therefore, preferable to use the same criteria as are described in the two preceding sections dealing with assessment and mitigation.

Just as it is easier and safer to predict visual impacts when good simulations are used, so it is simpler to compare actual and predicted impacts when the original simulation is at hand. Much of the text in visual impact reports tends to be vague and open to various interpretations: it is quite possible for a built project to conform technically with the wording of a visual impact assessment yet cause a surprising amount of public consternation over the degree of visual alteration. A simulation becomes a far more precise tool with which to judge the performance of a project in meeting expected goals or criteria for aesthetics. (See Chapters 7 and 8 for information on methods and examples of monitoring projects by the use of simulations.)

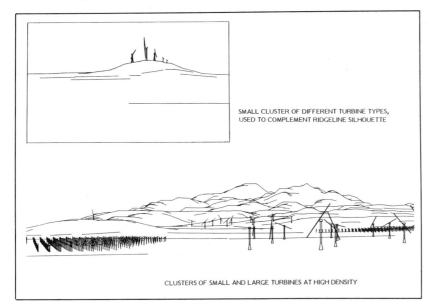

SMALL CLUSTER OF DIFFERENT TURBINE TYPES, USED TO COMPLEMENT RIDGELINE SILHOUETTE

CLUSTERS OF SMALL AND LARGE TURBINES AT HIGH DENSITY

Figure 3-13. Computer graphics showing method of mitigating the visual clutter of wind turbines by clustering them. © Dynamic Graphics, Inc.

REFERENCES

1. Litton, R. B., Jr. 1968. *Forest Landscape Description and Inventories: A Basis for Land Planning and Design.* U.S. Forest Service Research Paper PSW-49. Berkeley, Calif.: PSW Forest and Range Experiment Station.

2. U.S. Forest Service, 1974. *National Forest Landscape Management,* Vol. 2, Chap. 1, The Visual Management System. Agriculture Handbook No. 462. Washington, D.C.: U.S. Dept. of Agriculture.

3. U.S. Bureau of Land Management. 1980. *Visual Resource Management Program.* Washington, D.C.: U.S. Dept. of Interior.

4. Litton, R. B., Jr. 1984. *Visual Vulnerability of the Landscape: Control of Visual Quality.* U.S. Forest Service Research Paper WO-39. Washington, D.C.: USDA Forest Service.

5. Smardon, R. C., S. R. J. Sheppard, and S. Newman. 1984. "Visual Impact Assessment Manual." Occasional Paper No. ESF84-009, School of U.S. Landscape Architecture, SUNY College of Environmental Science and Forestry, Syracuse, New York.

6. Iverson, W. D. 1985. "And that's about the size of it: visual magnitude as a measurement of the physical landscape." *Landscape Journal* 4(1):14–22.

7. Craik, K. H. 1971. "The assessment of places." in *Advances in Psychological Assessment,* ed. P. McReynolds. Palo Alto, Calif.: Science and Behavior Books.

8. Dunn, M. C. 1976. "Landscape with photographs: testing the preference approach to landscape evaluation." *Journal of Environmental Management* 4(1):15–26.

9. Smardon, R. C., S. R. J. Sheppard, N. R. Feimer, and K. H. Craik. 1979. Final progress report on Visual Contrast Rating Research. Unpublished report prepared for U.S. Bureau of Land Management. Dept. of Landscape Architecture, University of California, Berkeley.

10. Hodgson, R. W., and R. L. Thayer. 1980. "Implied human influence reduces landscape beauty." *Landscape Planning* 7:171–79.

11. Litton, R. B., Jr. 1973. *Landscape Control Points: A Procedure for Predicting and Monitoring Visual Impacts.* U.S. Forest Service Research Paper PSW-91 Berkeley, Calif.: PSW Forest and Range Experiment Station.

Chapter **4**

FUNDAMENTALS AND PROBLEMS IN SIMULATION USE

The importance of the roles of visual simulation in visual resource analysis and generally in project planning makes it imperative that we understand how simulations work and that they be used properly. We know that where visual simulations are used, they may differ widely in form and content. Do all simulations present correct and relevant information? What do users think of the various simulations encountered? Do the pictures, rather than the scene or project itself, influence the user? In short, are the simulations typically used in project planning both fair and effective? Are they valid?

In order to answer these questions, we need to be able to judge simulations against a set of criteria. How do we distinguish a good simulation from a bad one?

A simulation is a communications tool. Like any other form of communication, therefore, it must get a message across to whomever is supposed to receive it. Moreover, the message, to be effective, must be believable or people will discount it. However, a visual simulation, unlike some other forms of communication, stands for something else; it represents a future environmental condition, and its purpose is to help viewers to visualize what they actually would see in

that environment. Consequently, the message or impression communicated by the simulation should be the right one, in the sense that it duplicates, as far as possible, the feelings that people would have at the real scene.

In the public arena, then, *good simulations* for project planning purposes can be defined as pictures or images that meet the following fundamental objectives: (1) they are understood by people, (2) they are convincing to people, and (3) they are unbiased.[1,2]

In Chapter 2, we discussed the benefits of using good simulations (see Fig. 2-25a). Some of the potential consequences of using poor simulations were delineated in Figure 2-25b. This chapter reviews the quality of simulations typically used today in terms of how well they fulfill the fundamental objectives. In so doing, we will see what general kinds of problems emerge with simulations in practice, and begin to gain a better understanding of how these problems might be addressed by application of specific principles (Chapter 6).

The discussion of fundamentals and problems of simulation use in this and subsequent chapters is based largely upon research carried out by the author.[3] A full summary of this research is provided in Appendix D, but as general background, it may be helpful to provide here a brief overview of the methods employed. This research reviewed more than three hundred projects and analyzed a large number of visual simulations used on more than thirty actual projects. The study investigated the interrelationships among three factors: the nature of the simulation, people's reactions to the simulation, and the actual built projects. Simulations were compared systematically with the actual appearance of the corresponding built projects and differences noted. A group of 146 environmental planners and designers was asked to judge the projects in question in terms of their aesthetic qualities, based on either the simulated or actual views. They were also asked to give their impressions on the quality of the simulations. Thus, it was possible to gain an idea of how understandable the simulations were, how convincing they were to users, and whether they biased the participants' feelings toward the project when compared with the real thing. It was also possible to examine the potential causes of simulation problems by relating them to particular properties of the simulations themselves, as discussed in subsequent chapters.

THE PROBLEM OF POOR COMMUNICATION (LACK OF UNDERSTANDING)

If a message cannot be understood, it cannot be effective. Simulations should be understandable. A simulation is understandable if users can gain sufficient meaningful information from it without ambiguity, confusion, or difficulties in recognition. Conversely, simulations can be hard to understand if they are unclear, chaotic, or incomplete, or if they contain obvious errors.

The following comments illustrate situations where necessary visual information was not clearly communicated. In most cases, they are quoted from actual project case histories where simulations were used; often, such observations are recorded in the Response to Comments section of environmental impact reports. Other statements come from participants in the author's research study of simulations used on actual projects.[3]

The EIR mentions some adverse impacts on views, but provides no detailed discussion or visual illustration of these impacts so that the reader can judge their significance.[4]

The renderings do not show the proper scale, texture, or character of the project.[5]

The photographs are interesting but should have houses superimposed to be really helpful. Is the vertical scale true or exaggerated? If the roads were colored, it would be easier to decipher.[6]

The report contains insufficient graphic or explanatory material by which to judge the contention that the aesthetic impact of the project will be beneficial.[7]

[The simulation is] too abstract to be meaningful.[3]

It is not uncommon for interpreters of a simulation to complain about its confusing or incomplete nature. The most frequent complaint centers on a lack of design detail: there is insufficient information to demonstrate the nature and appearance of the project. For example, the technique of showing abstract building masses or "envelopes," even if montaged on a site photograph, often fuels requests from the public for more information and/or revised simulations that show more architectural detail and character (Fig. 4-1).

Omission of sufficient views and site context to permit people to judge the project's compatibility with its surroundings is another frequent problem. The simulation should provide the appropriate information for more than just the project, because interpreters need to understand the effects on the project setting too.

Other problems stem from too much information in the picture. With multiple overlays of line drawings for example, so many lines may be superimposed that it becomes difficult to distinguish what is what and how objects relate to one another (Fig. 4-1*b*). Problems in understanding a simulation usually occur when those who are preparing or presenting the simulation fail to consider the type of people who will be interpreting it, or the kind of information they will want to get from it. This leads to simulations being used that are unsuitable for the particular audience or for the issues of concern. An architect or engineer may be able to interpret a set of complex draw-

a

Figure 4-1. Photomontage of a proposed office building, used in a draft Environmental Impact Report (EIR) *(a)*; a more detailed photomontage, produced in the final EIR after requests from the public for more information on appearance *(b).*

b

ings, but the general public may not. Media that can greatly assist professional analysis of a project can confuse and frustrate local residents.

If simulations cause confusion or uncertainty in the minds of those trying to interpret them, they are likely to be ignored or become the focus of conflict. Arguments can easily arise over the correct interpretation of the simulation. Either way, decisions will be made without the correct visual information, by guesswork or interpretation of written or verbal opinions. Possibly, decisions may even have to be postponed until more

information can be provided or the existing information is repackaged for easier consumption.

It is important in visual analysis to distinguish between people's understanding of the simulation and their understanding of the project itself. The aim here should be for the *simulation* to be understandable, and not necessarily the project. Thus, if a proposed structure is very complex and would appear to be chaotic or confusing in reality, then a simulation of its appearance should clearly show it as such, and should not necessarily attempt to "explain" how the project works.

THE PROBLEM OF DISTRUST (LACK OF CREDIBILITY)

This is the situation in which a simulation gets a message across, but the interpreter of the message does not believe it. Simulations should be believable and, ideally, users ought not to be skeptical of them. A simulation is *convincing* if the people who are interpreting it believe that the real scene would look like or be like that which is simulated, or that the information contained in the simulation is correct.

The following comments illustrate situations in which the credibility of simulations is in question. They are reproduced from either the actual case histories where simulations have been used, or from statements made by participants in the author's research on simulations used in actual projects.[3]

The drawings superimposed on the photographs are out of scale. Close attention should be given to making this pictorial representation as accurate and representative of the actual visual relationship of the project with the surroundings as possible.[8]

We would again refute many of the photographs used that have the proposed hotel superimposed. . . . We object to the inaccuracy of the presentation on this critical area of discussion. . . . We object most strenuously to Figure 13. . . . The scale here is absurd.[8]

[Members of the Club] are seriously concerned that graphic illustrations of the project do not accurately reflect, in terms of proportion and scale, the size and impact of the project.[9]

The photographic exhibits have several shortcomings, e.g., distortions of size, poor vantage points, grading not accurately shown, and units deleted.[10]

The sketches included in the report give an unrealistic view of the project. They show no people or automobiles, and their perspective makes it seem as though the project is tucked away in the distance.[11]

Sometimes you see drawings like this one . . . you can see all the clichés . . . with which someone is trying to buy off the com-

munity. When that building gets built, it ain't going to look like that.[3]

Review of both actual project case histories and professionals' responses to simulations indicates widespread credibility problems. In the author's survey of planners' responses to simulations used in actual project applications, the vast majority of comments about simulations were negative.[3] In particular, many users express an unwillingness to believe in the simulation. Complaints about simulation take the form of uncertainty ("I can understand it but I don't know whether to believe it"), or skepticism ("I don't believe it, and think that the real scene would be different").

Planners and other environmental professionals participating in the author's study expressed a considerable lack of confidence in most simulations examined. When asked to rate their confidence that the real scenes would look like those depicted in the simulations, the average response was "uncertain"; some 38 percent of the professionals participating felt fairly skeptical or very skeptical about the simulations.

In some cases, simulation credibility is so low that members of the public have prepared their own drawings of a proposed project to dramatize the alleged failings of the original simulations (Fig. 4-2).

a

b

Figure 4-2. Simulation of proposed hotel building on San Francisco Bay, presented in a draft EIR *(a);* sketch of the same view by a member of the public, submitted to indicate perceived problems in the original simulations *(b).*

At the other extreme, users may be fooled into thinking the simulation is actually a photograph or film taken at the site of a built project (Fig. 4-3 and Plate 12).[12] In fact, people may sometimes be too ready to believe in some simulations, just because they look real, regardless of the information they contain. Even nonrealistic media can be believed too readily; for example, it is often assumed that a computer graphic must be accurate simply because it was drawn by a computer, when, in fact, the computer may have been given inadequate or inaccurate data.

Among the author's study participants, line drawings in particular tended to produce skepticism, while full-color and tonal renderings left them uncertain. They had most confidence in detailed, full-color models and modified photographs (created by retouching and photomontage). Similar results have been found in everyday practice. Renderings and models, in particular, provide opportunities for artistic ex-

a

b

Figure 4-3. View of a model *(b)* which, when shown in a movie sequence to study participants at U.C. Berkeley, was mistaken for film footage of a real drive through the landscape *(a)*.

pression and artistic license which can cause distrust. Slick graphics and other presentation features, such as music or birdsong, often are criticized as attempts to bias the audience. It is quite possible for simulations to look ''too good to believe.'' Conversely, sketchy or amateurish simulations also are prone to criticism. People may even equate poor quality of the simulation with poor quality of project design.

Distrust usually occurs when simulations are apparently incorrect or apparently misleading. The key factor here is not whether the simulation is actually wrong, but whether it is perceived to be wrong. Specific causes for distrust of simulations are discussed further in Chapter 6.

Lack of confidence in simulations can lead to conflicting opinions on the project among observers, and to negative attitudes toward the project or the review process. A feeling may arise that the simulation is an attempt to hoodwink the audience or deprive them of important information, whether or not the simulation is actually incorrect or misleading. This can result in public controversy and can cause costly delay in obtaining a decision. Simulations may have to be revised or created all over again before project decisions can be made.

There is, therefore, a strong link between the credibility of simulations and the acceptability of the project to the public and agencies.

The author has found in interviews with planners that some of them automatically and deliberately compensate for perceived bias in simulations, assuming that developers' drawings normally exaggerate the positive aspects of the design and that the actual impacts of the development would be more negative. The danger in this is that some drawings may be more correct than others, and the planner may not know which aspects of the project are the most biased.

THE PROBLEM OF BIAS

If the interpreter of a simulation understands and believes its message, but that message is incorrect, then the interpreter is likely to get the wrong impression and make a poor judgment. Even if the interpreter does not believe the simulation, he or she may not visualize the correct situation and may still make a poor judgment.

The most important criterion of a good simulation is that it should be fair and unbiased. A simulation is *unbiased* if it leads to user reactions and judgments similar to those that would be obtained with views of the real scene. This is what environmental psychologists call "response equivalence."[1] A misleading simulation is one that leads to a biased reaction or judgment, different from that which the real view would elicit. People may misinterpret a picture and obtain false information from it. They may like the simulated scene more than they would the real scene (favorable bias) or they may like it less than the real scene (unfavorable bias). The use of the term *bias* for simulation does not mean that the preparers themselves are necessarily biased. As will be shown, simulation bias or deceptiveness may be unintentional and can be due to many factors.

The following comments are reproduced either from actual case histories of projects that have been built, or from the statements of participants in the author's research evaluating simulations used on actual projects.[3]

The slide show presented by the [consultant] as a supplement to the EIR was completely misleading as the buildings were hidden by numerous dense, oversize model trees. The trees are naturally not there now and due to wind exposure of the site will not be as presented for at least 15 years, if then. The photos of 4-storey buildings being hidden by 4-storey high trees was deliberately misleading—not an unbiased "visual aid."[13]

The artist's portrayal of what the inland route would look like . . . is totally inaccurate. Because these exhibits showed all the cut-and-fill slopes completely revegetated, they led people to draw incorrect conclusions about the inland route. This was a deliberate distortion to influence the outcome of the decision.[14]

The simulation graphics . . . don't do justice to the silhouette (outline) of the actual project.[3]

The simulation looks like a cabin in the woods. Actually, it's an eyesore.[3]

[The simulation] would deceive the typical citizen participant, but would impress him.[3]

I think the drawing plays up the dam and makes it a very spectacular thing. . . . It also makes it something nice and crisp, which if you notice over there is completely erroneous. . . . It doesn't show any of the grading or anything, which you would really have to consider part of the project.[3]

The author found that three-quarters of the simulations that were examined were significantly misleading in people's judgments of scenic quality and/or the project's visual impact.[3] In other words, in most cases the landscape containing the project looked better or worse in the simulation than it did in real life (or in a photograph of the real scene). This does not necessarily mean that one was liked while the other was

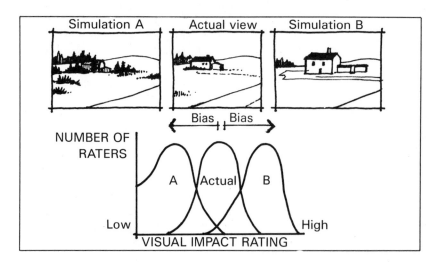

Figure 4-4. Hypothetical relationships in simulation bias.

disliked, but that one was liked or disliked considerably more than the other.

Of those simulations that were misleading, about 50 percent looked better to the users than did the view of the actual project. The other 50 percent looked worse than did the actual view. Biased simulations, therefore, do not always favor the project or developer.

It is not easy to measure how much bias occurs with a given simulation. People react differently to simulations according to their knowledge of the site, their attitude toward the project, their familiarity with simulations, and many other factors. The most that can be said usually is that a certain simulation tends to mislead more people than another, or, for example, that more people dislike the project in the simulation than in actual views. Figure 4-4 illustrates hypothetical relationships in which significant bias occurs in average responses even though there is considerable overlap between individuals' responses to simulations and their responses to reality. Similar relationships have been found with actual simulations.[3]

Simulations may be misleading in one kind of judgment or response, such as visual impact of the project, and fair in another, such as overall attractiveness of the scene. The author's research suggests, however, that simulations are rarely biased favorably toward the project on one criterion and biased unfavorably toward it on another.

The causes of simulation bias are poorly understood. The causes of confusion and distrust can readily be discovered simply by listening to people's reactions to simulations and asking them questions; interpretation of what people at the time think is misleading in a simulation can be dangerous, however. It has been shown that some simulations that were thought to be misleading actually led to unbiased judgment of a project's appearance.[3] The only real test for bias requires analysis of people's reactions to the built project; because systematic postconstruction evaluation is so rare, very little reliable information is available to indicate how much bias is occurring, let alone what the causes are. Although it is common to hear of instances where simulations are believed in hindsight to have been misleading, very few research studies have systematically measured the amount of bias caused by different variables.

Consequently, we can only surmise general patterns and causes of simulation bias from scattered bits and pieces of evidence. Clearly, there are many potential factors that could cause simulations to be misleading. Again, these can be problems in either the simulation or the interpreter. The probable causes of bias in simulations are discussed in depth in Chapter 6.

Misleading simulations can result in poor decisions based on incorrect assumptions. Projects may be approved that arouse public concern when built, or projects may be needlessly rejected or redesigned. Design problems and opportunities for enhancement may be missed; conversely, expensive mitigation measures may be needlessly demanded. Unfavorable bias in simulations may help inflame opposition to proposed projects, while favorable bias may persuade decision-makers unwittingly to permit construction of substandard or otherwise unacceptable projects. There are many examples of projects which, once built, have become objects of derision and intense public hostility due to their appearance. Sometimes the effect is so strong that removal of the project is recommended and even carried out, representing a tremendous waste of time, money, resources, and effort. There are some notable examples:

- The destruction of the Embarcadero Freeway along San Francisco's waterfront has been debated and proposed by various city agencies over the years, with a potential cost of millions of dollars, based largely on visual arguments (see Fig. 2-26).
- In a lawsuit against several major wind-turbine companies and the Bureau of Land Management, on grounds of aesthetic damage to the recreational image of the area, the City of Palm Springs demanded that several wind developments in the most conspicuous locations be removed (Fig. 4-5).
- The U.S. Army at San Francisco's Presidio was forced to demolish a proposed post office building before it was completed, because of public opposition and lawsuits based largely on visual impacts at Crissey Field.

Figure 4-5. Wind turbines in San Gorgonio Pass which were among those studied for feasibility of removal on grounds of visual impact.

REFERENCES

1. Appleyard, D. 1977. "Understanding professional media." In *Human Behavior and Environment,* Vol. 1, ed. Altman and Wohlwill, New York: Plenum Press, pp. 43–88.

2. Sheppard, S. R. J. 1983. "How credible are visual simulations?" *Landscape Architecture* 73 (1):83.

3. Sheppard, S. R. J. 1982. "Landscape portrayals: their use, accuracy, and validity in simulating proposed landscape changes." Ph.D. diss., University of California, Berkeley.

4. Mead, R. A. 1975. Comments on Sycamore Avenue Extension Draft EIR, Mill Valley, Calif., 26 January 1975.

5. Don Olson and Associates. 1975. Comment on Glendon Retreat Hotel and Recording Studio Draft EIR, Marin County, Calif., 7 November 1975, in EIR Addendum, December 1975.

6. City of Novato. 1975. Response to comments on the Marin Hills Project EIR, Novato, Calif.

7. City of Sausalito. 1975. Comments by K. Arnaudo on the Richardson Highlands/Marin Headlands EIR, in the Precise Development Plan Phase 2, Addendum, Appendix VI, Sausalito, Calif., 8 August 1975.

8. Littoral Development Co. 1978. Comments on the Whaler's Point Hotel Draft EIR, 16 June 1978, in Whaler's Point Hotel Final EIR and Response to Comments, Vol. III, October 1978.

9. Almonte District Improvement Club. 1978. Comments on public meeting, in Whaler's Point Hotel Draft EIR, Vol. II, Technical Appendices.

10. Marin County Planning Department. 1975. Staff report on Anderson Rowe Ranch Draft EIR, 19 February 1975.

11. Kruskal, T. 1973. Comments on Tomales Bay Lodge EIR, 28 March 1973.

12. Craik, K. H., D. Appleyard, and G. E. McKechnie. 1980. *Impressions of a Place: Effects of Media and Familiarity among Environmental Professionals.* Research Technical Report. Berkeley, Calif.: Institute of Personality Assessment and Research, University of California.

13. Hansen, C. 1973. Comment on public hearing for Shelter Ridge Development EIR, Mill Valley, Calif., 4 April 1973.

14. Author unknown. 1985. Public comment on the Devil's Slide Draft EIS, in Devil's Slide Final EIS, Vol. II. San Francisco: California Department of Transportation.

Chapter 5

THE SIMULATION PROCESS

So far, we have reviewed the benefits of using good simulations and the consequences of using poor simulations. We have also identified the fundamental qualities of a good simulation—that it be understandable, believable, and unbiased.

Before we can establish principles to follow in achieving these objectives, we must understand the context in which such principles may influence simulation quality. This chapter considers the typical simulation process: What chain of decisions affects the outcome of a particular simulation (and, potentially, the project itself)? What procedural constraints and other factors are there that may have a bearing on the comprehension, credibility, and bias of simulations?

Figure 5-1 presents a simplified diagram of the typical simulation process. It can be considered as a side loop of the flow chart of the overall project planning process shown in Figure 2-1. It occurs somewhere between the initial planning of the project and its permitting or approval. Once a project is defined and the need for simulation has been established, the simulation process runs through several phases as shown in Figure 5-1. A method of simulation is selected, the views to be simulated are chosen, simulation images are prepared, simulations are presented,

and they are interpreted by the audience with a certain degree of understanding, credibility, and bias.

In practice, the actual simulation process can vary substantially from that shown, and be more or less complex. The process varies with the reason for preparing simulations. A designer sketching out architectural concepts as part of his own design process seldom bothers to mount and display each drawing—he responds almost instantaneously to the lines he is creating. However, he still chooses the type of pen and paper to use, the angle of view to be shown, and the number of drawings to show to the client later. In the public planning arena, the process tends to follow the diagram more closely. Some simulation media fit the conceptual process better than others: if a three-dimensional model is to be displayed in a public meeting, for example, there may be no need to select specific views—people can inspect it from any angle they choose.

Depending upon the stage in project planning when the simulation process begins, one of two kinds of simulation may be used:

1. *Generic simulations* tend to be used early in project planning, during siting or preliminary

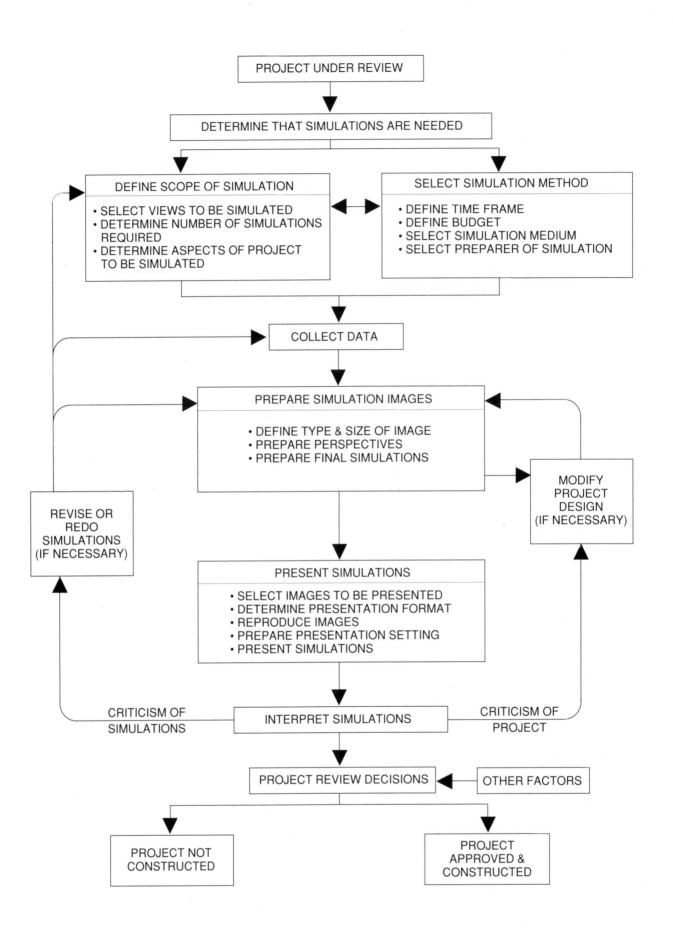

Figure 5-1. Simplified simulation process.

review. They show the typical appearance of a proposed project, rather than a specific design or exact location. For example, people may want to get an idea of how a residential project would look on a hillside, regardless of the house designs, or how well a typical steel-lattice transmission tower would fit in a lowland farming landscape (see Fig. 2-6). In such cases, it is neither necessary nor feasible to have exact design specifications for structures and actual structure locations. Instead, a typical structure type and generally representative location may be selected.

2. *Specific simulations* show the anticipated appearance of a project once it has been designed in detail, according to working drawings, exact locations, and design specifications.

Most of the decisions outlined in Figure 5-1 need to be made with both kinds of simulation. Generic simulations need not necessarily be conceptual or cartoonish. There is no reason why a general situation cannot be shown in full realistic detail, so long as it is made clear that the simulation is based upon assumed conditions instead of specific designs. Similarly, specific simulations need not necessarily be fully detailed. The distinction between generic and specific simulations is not, therefore, based upon the look of the simulations, but upon the type of information used in preparing them. Simply because the information in a generic simulation is not based on a detailed design does not mean that the fundamental objectives of understanding, credibility, and fairness can be dispensed with.

An important point to note from the process diagram is the separation between creating the original simulation image and presenting the simulation in its final format. Different combinations of media can be used. Most of the images prepared with the media shown in Table 5-1 can be presented in any of the formats listed in the table. Much can happen to a simulation on its way from the desk where it was prepared to the eye of the interpreter. Images will be reproduced, cropped, spliced together with other material, enlarged, reduced, labeled, and sometimes selectively omitted. In considering the quality of a simulation, then, we need to consider both the original image and the final presentation.

From the standpoint of possible influences on simulation quality, it is clear that at any point in the simulation process, numerous factors can potentially lead to confusion, distrust, or biased responses in the audience. Theory and common sense tell us that responses to simulations may be affected by

- the data and methods used in preparing the simulations
- the original simulation medium
- the abilities of the preparer
- the presentation format

In looking for principles for good simulation, however, it will not help us merely to suggest right or wrong simulation media, or to define the minimum professional qualifications of simulation preparers. The uses and applications of visual simulation in project planning are too diverse. More importantly, the above factors all interact; as a result, a good simulation technique

TABLE 5-1. TYPES OF SIMULATION MEDIA

Original Simulation Images	Presentation Formats
Renderings	Report page
—full color	—black & white
—black & white (tonal)	—full color
—black & white (line)	Mounted boards
Photomontage	Projected color slides
Photo retouching	Color or black & white prints
Multiple projection of photographs/images	Simulation booth with backlit transparencies
Altered video image (image processing)	Computer monitor
Computer perspective	Video monitor or TV screen
—wire frame	Film-projection or video-projection screen
—solid modeling	Model on dais or wall
—texture mapping	Model with modelscope or controlled viewing positions
Dynamic computer perspective	Hologram
—wire frame	Site visit/field trip
—solid modeling	
—texture mapping	
Film or video animation by montage (e.g., blue matte)	
Hologram	
Model	
—simplified	
—detailed	
Full-scale mock-up	
—scale markers	
—project replica	

carried out by one kind of user may backfire with another. The entire situation is too complex and too variable for us to jump to simplistic or convenient conclusions.

The literature on visual simulation has been too preoccupied with media and the differences among them, when many other subtle and not-so-subtle influences may be at work. Simply to accept that a simulation is good or bad, based upon the medium employed, would be to endorse unsubstantiated opinions (such as the often-heard planner's adage that "all renderings lie") and potentially to denigrate an entire profession of illustrators and renderers. What we need are some guiding principles, some common denominators, that can cut across the infinite combinations of media, users, and projects. These also need to be recognizable, meaningful properties of simulations that can be described objectively and perhaps even be measured. Chapter 6 provides principles that are meant to fulfill these needs.

There are, of course, other possible influences on how simulations are interpreted, beyond the nature of the simulations themselves. They include the type of project or issue being simulated, the preparer or presenter of the simulations, the information given out at the same time as the simulations are presented, and the composition and attitudes of the audience at the time. Many of these influences may be beyond the control of the simulation preparer. The following examples illustrate these points:

PROJECT TYPE.   It is possible that the visual effects of certain distinctive kinds of projects, such as major power plants in rural areas, can be reliably predicted regardless of the quality of simulation used (at least in close-up views) because they are known to be very large-scale, conspicuous, and industrial in character (Fig. 5-2).

PREPARERS AND PRESENTERS.   The identity of the people responsible for a simulation may generate skepticism and distrust automatically. For example, certain architects have a reputation for design renderings that bear little resemblance to the finished building. Often, simulations presented by developers of a project are expected to be biased. This is a risk whenever simulations are prepared by people with a stake in the success or failure of a project.

Figure 5-2. Large projects such as power plants, here shown in a photosimulation, are likely to be rated as having considerable visual impact, regardless of how they are simulated.

ACCOMPANYING INFORMATION.   Information presented along with the simulation can markedly affect how people respond. Zube asked people what they felt about different modifications to the appearance of Niagara Falls shown in a realistic model.[1] He found that people who were not informed about the natural results of erosion at the Falls preferred a version of the model that showed a neater, more orderly arrangement of rocks and water; people who had had an explanation of the erosion process tended to prefer a more broken, rocky appearance.

AUDIENCE.   The nature of the audience or interpreters may predetermine how a simulation is received. For instance, local residents at public hearings on nuclear waste repositories or nuclear power plants may be expected to be critical of any information presented on the project; a certain amount of bias in people's responses is to be expected even with a good simulation.

There are, therefore, several situations in which simulations are more likely to be mistrusted or misinterpreted, and these situations are considered in the next chapter on simulation principles. The primary emphasis, however, is placed upon properties of the simulations themselves.

REFERENCE

1. Zube, E. H. 1980. *Environmental Evaluation: Perception and Public Policy.* Monterey, Calif.: Brooks/Cole Publishing Co.

Chapter 6

PRINCIPLES FOR SIMULATION USE

Some of the general problems in simulation use have been discussed in Chapter 4. Chapter 5 described the various points in the process where the quality of simulation can be compromised. This chapter focuses on the aspects of simulation believed to be important in assuring good simulations. Which specific properties of a simulation directly determine its comprehension, credibility, and bias? What causes the problems that occur in everyday use of simulations? What guiding principles can we follow to avoid such problems?

In attempting to answer these questions, we can classify or categorize the different properties potentially affecting simulation quality; we can review the evidence indicating if and how they affect simulation quality; and we can draw from that evidence suggestions on how to produce simulations in the future. Because of the scarcity of hard evidence, however, particularly with regard to simulation bias (as noted in Chapter 4), it must be recognized that the principles emerging from this analysis are, in large part, based on theory and on the professional opinion of the author and others. As research proceeds, these principles should be examined critically and revised if necessary. In the meantime, the analysis pre-

sented in this chapter can serve as a road map for future research, in laying out the important simulation properties that need to be tested further.

A combination of literature review, original research, and practical experience suggests that the following five properties of simulations determine their comprehension, credibility, and bias, and could form the basis for comprehensive principles:

1. *Representativeness*—the degree to which a simulation or set of simulations represents important and typical views of a project
2. *Accuracy*—the similarity in appearance between the simulated scene and the real scene as it would look after the project has been built
3. *Visual Clarity*—the degree to which the detail, parts, and overall content of the simulation can be clearly distinguished and recognized
4. *Interest*—the degree to which a simulation or set of simulations engages or holds the interest of its audience
5. *Legitimacy*—the extent to which the correct-

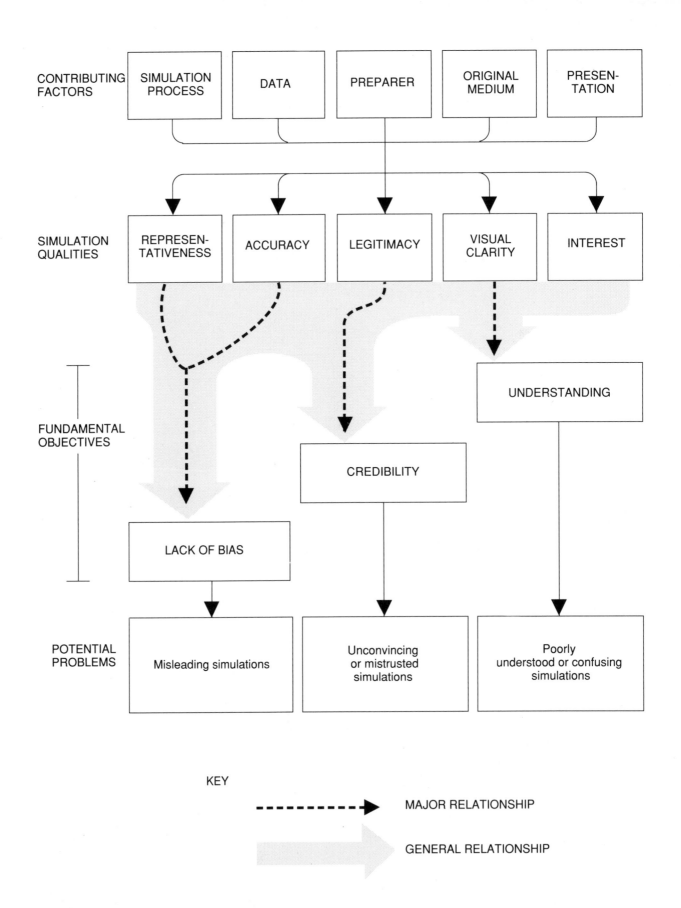

Figure 6-1. Factors contributing to potential problems with simulations.

ness of the simulation is demonstrated and defensible

These five properties can explain much of the variation in quality of simulations typically used today. Figure 6-1 indicates how these properties may determine the ease of understanding, credibility, and bias in simulations. Table 6-1 summarizes the major relationships theorized here.

Whether or not a simulation is well understood and its message absorbed is dictated mostly by the visual clarity and interest of the final presentation. The credibility of simulations may be affected by any of the factors but can be related most directly to the legitimacy factor during presentation. Simulation bias is believed to be influenced most by how representative and accurate the simulations are. Since these two attributes seem to exert the most influence on the ultimate validity of simulations, and apply to both the production of original images and to final presentations, they will be discussed in the most detail.

Recognition of the five properties—representativeness, accuracy, visual clarity, interest, and legitimacy—provides a set of criteria or principles for simulation use, against which any simulation can be judged. Where one or more of these attributes are lacking in a simulation, a potentially serious problem exists if the simulation is to be used in project planning. Thus, *poor simulations* can be defined as pictures or images that

- show unrepresentative views and/or fail to show representative views
- are inaccurate
- are visually indistinct, muddled, or distracting
- are boring or overly entertaining

- are without evidence demonstrating their legitimacy

In the sections that follow, each principle in turn is discussed and its significance explained. The occurrence of problems where these principles are not followed in practice is described, and the reasons for their occurrence are examined. Lastly, the simulation characteristics required to avoid such problems are outlined.

PRINCIPLE 1: SIMULATIONS SHOULD BE REPRESENTATIVE

Definition

A set of simulations is representative if it shows important views of the project, and shows the project in typical views and conditions. An important view of a project is one which gives a view that is distinctly different from other important views and in reality would be seen by significant numbers of people on a regular basis.

The number of simulations required to be fully representative depends upon the nature of the project and site, but it is clear that in many cases, a single view cannot express all of the pertinent aspects of a project's appearance (Fig. 6-2). There may be several viewpoints—for example, along highways, in residential areas or parks—that are affected differently due to distance and angle of view. A single simulation is like a single point on a graph: it is impossible to tell from that how conditions vary. Two simulations, like two points connected by a line on a

TABLE 6-1. THEORETICAL RELATIONSHIPS BETWEEN SIMULATION PROPERTIES AND FUNDAMENTAL OBJECTIVES

		Fundamental Objectives		
		Understanding	Credibility	Lack of Bias
Simulation Properties	Representativeness	●	•	●
	Accuracy	●	●	●
	Visual clarity	●	●	•
	Interest	●	●	•
	Legitimacy	•	●	•

Key:
Major Influence ●   Moderate Influence ●   Minor Influence •

a

b

c

Figure 6-2. Existing view *(a)* and photosimulations *(b* and *c)* used to represent different views of the proposed Trans-Pacific Center in Oakland, California; note the effect of distance on scale relationships.

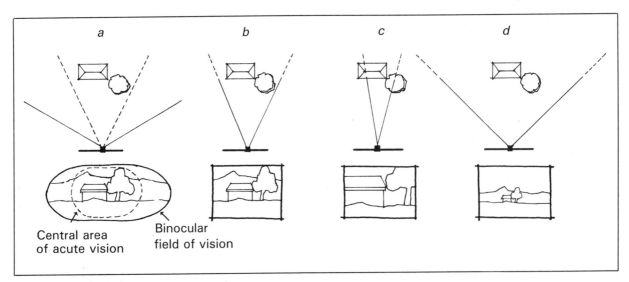

Figure 6-3. Comparisons of the field-of-view of the eye and camera lenses: human eye *(a)*; standard camera lens (35 mm camera with 50 mm lens) *(b)*; telephoto lens (35 mm camera with 115 mm lens) *(c)*; wide-angle lens (35 mm camera with 25 mm lens) *(d)*.

graph, begin to tell a story, to describe a pattern or relationship; they double the amount of visual information available for decision-making, and suggest the possibility of other conditions to be considered (which may or may not be demonstrated by additional simulations).

In any given view, the *field-of-view*—the amount of a scene that is included in the simulation—is important. In real views, our sight covers almost 180 degrees from side to side, including peripheral vision, but we focus generally on objects within the central 50-degree range (Fig. 6-3*a*). In a simulation, the frame or edge of the picture (usually rectangular) limits the breadth and height of the scene that is shown. Given a particular viewpoint and direction of view, a simulation may show a wider or narrower view than we would see on-site. Photographs taken with wide-angle, standard, and telephoto lenses are examples of different fields-of-view (Figs. 6-3*b, c, d*). A simulation based upon a telephoto-lens photograph, for example, may be unrepresentative in that it omits part of the scene that forms the context for the project.

There may be marked changes in project appearance with different *viewing conditions* (for example, lighting, weather, season, and project age). A simulation may or may not be representative based on the viewing conditions shown.

Most static simulation images will, strictly speaking, be somewhat unrepresentative because it is virtually impossible to view an actual scene without some sort of motion in the observer or the landscape (or both). In fact, many views typically are obtained while the observer is

moving, and this can radically affect how a scene or project is viewed. Even where dynamic or animated simulations (simulations that show motion) are used, they may be more or less representative depending on the direction and angle of view and the speed at which they are presented.

Significance

Selection of viewpoints and viewing conditions for simulation is one of the most crucial and difficult steps in preparing good simulations. Without a representative set of simulations, certain aspects of the project design are likely to be ignored. While a simulation may show the view that one group of residents would obtain, the impacts on other residents with different views may not be similar and their concerns may fail to be addressed if their views are not simulated. There is potential for the simulations to be misleading in terms of overall visual impact of the project, particularly if they omit the typical worst-case view or show the project only in unusually favorable (or unfavorable) conditions. Omission of important views also can hurt the credibility of simulations presented. On the other hand, simulation of only the worst-case view, particularly if it represents a very brief view, may leave the viewer with an impression of a more dominant project than would result in real life.

Incorrect field-of-view may also bias a simulation: the narrower the field-of-view in the simulation, the more likely it is to mislead users because it may exclude surrounding objects that

a

b

Figure 6-4. Sketch of proposed ski-jump structure, used in an environmental impact report for the Winter Olympic Games at Lake Placid, New York *(a)*; photograph of actual view taken with a 55 mm lens, revealing a wider field of view with important contextual objects (historical monument to John Brown) *(b)*.

a   *b*

Figure 6-5. Comparison of two photosimulations showing distant proposed power line in the Gore Pass area of Colorado: during daylight *(a)*; at dusk *(b)*, shown in response to public concerns for impacts on sunset views. From *Foundations for Visual Project Review,* R. C. Smardon, J. Palmer, and J. Felleman (eds.) © 1986 John Wiley & Sons.

strongly influence the overall scene (Fig. 6-4). Depending on the nature of what is omitted, the bias may be favorable or unfavorable to the project.

Use of static simulations when views would actually be obtained from moving vehicles may lead viewers to focus upon detailed or foreground elements (such as roadside telephone poles, bushes, and fences) that would be seen in reality only as a blur or succession of ordinary repeated objects. This may compete with the visual dominance of projects at a distance from the road, whereas in real views the project alone stands out. Static simulations are capable of showing only a tiny fraction of all possible views of a project. Dynamic simulations showing moving views present far more information on which to judge the impacts and quality of a project, and therefore should reduce the possibility of bias. At the same time, the ability to study and analyze static simulations may compensate for the quick impressions obtained in a moving image and come closer to the responses obtained through familiarity with the real project.

For certain kinds of projects, static simulations may underemphasize how noticeable moving objects can be. Motion of smoke, dust plumes, water, machinery, or vehicles can be very important in attracting attention to projects such as cooling towers, oil refineries, flood-control structures, strip mines, highways, oil-drilling sites, and wind turbines. The repetitive flashing of strobe lights on tall structures is a potential annoyance to viewers that is difficult to simulate without dynamic techniques.

Simulations that show unusual or short-lived conditions, such as dramatic shadows, rainbows, or vivid cloud effects, may create a more favorable impression of the project than would more commonly occur in reality. This potential source of bias is especially likely with modified photographs which can capture and enhance such effects (Plate 13) or with full-color renderings where artist's license is exercised. It should be recognized, however, that some ephemeral conditions (for example, sunsets seen across a bay, or fog obscuring distant mountains) do occur repeatedly and can be of major importance in considering project impacts (Fig. 6-5 and Plate 14).

Problems in Practice

1. In the author's survey, almost half of the projects that had been simulated were shown in a single ground view or an aerial view (Fig. 6-6).[1] On average, less than half of the important views of the project were represented in the simulations. The degree to which the views shown are representative is often questioned by the audience; additional illustrations from other viewpoints sometimes are requested by local residents or planners. A common criticism in environmental reports is a lack of simulations representing alternative designs or locations described in the report.

2. Many simulations show views that are atypical; some views are not easily attainable by everyday observers in real life (Fig. 6-7), and some simulated views appear to be largely imaginary (Fig. 6-8).

a

b

Figure 6-6. Aerial view *(a)* and ground view *(b)* of power plant show very different visual relationships.

Figure 6-7. Rendering *(a)* from viewpoint overlooking proposed power plant, and actual photo *(b)* showing real view blocked by visitor center.

70

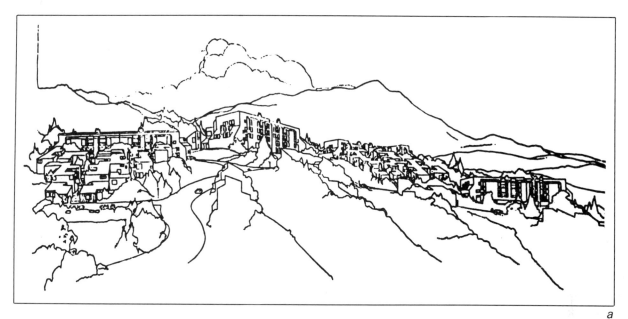

a

b

Figure 6-8. Sketch *(a)* of proposed housing development; photograph *(b)* was the closest the author could get to re-creating the same view in reality.

3. Very few projects are depicted in the form of a series of views to represent changes in appearance along travel routes. An impression or abstraction of movement occasionally is created by using a sequence of static views, or by inserting static simulations as pauses in moving footage of actual landscapes.

4. None of the projects surveyed by the author had simulations that portrayed motion on the part of the observer, although this is quite possible with a variety of techniques. Static views remain the rule, and moving or animated simulations the exception in practice. Truly dynamic simulations, capable of presenting a moving view of a proposed environment are, however, beginning to be used by such means as animated computer graphics, manipulated footage of video or movie film, or footage filmed with a periscope camera or modelscope lens moving through a scale model (Fig. 6-9). Even among dynamic simulations, however, there have been few attempts to depict movement of objects within the scene.

5. Very seldom do simulations show changes in project appearance with time, and few even acknowledge that the appearance as simulated may vary as time goes by and conditions change. Simulations of projects in different lighting conditions (see Fig. 6-5) are very rare, as are nocturnal simulations,[2] even though some projects have greater visual impacts at night than during the day due to illumination. Longer-term changes are sometimes simulated where the reclamation of disturbed areas may take many years, as in landfill, forest, or mining projects, but seldom does this happen with other projects. A rare exception, developed for general planning purposes, is a videotape of a typical suburban tract that shows changes with pro-

Figure 6-9. Frames from a film depicting motion through a scale model of Marin County, California.

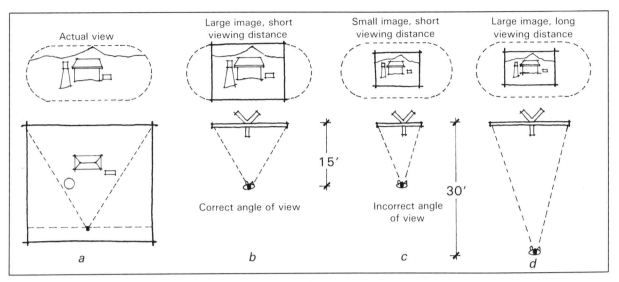

Figure 6-10. Effects of variation in image size and image viewing distance.

jected demographic trends over a thirty-year period.[3]

6. Most simulations (over 50 percent in the author's survey) show a field-of-view that corresponds roughly to that in a normal camera with a 50 to 60 mm lens, approximately 40 to 45 degrees in breadth of field. However, some simulations have much narrower fields-of-view; this may not be apparent from looking at the simulation alone, and so may give an impression that the project has greater dominance in the view than it really would have, or that it is the only important object in the landscape (see Fig. 6-4). A field-of-view of much less than 45 degrees usually omits important surrounding context.

Conversely, a few simulations show very wide fields-of-view and, depending upon how much sky and foreground is included, this too may not be recognized. The project may appear to be less dominant than it really would be, especially in cases where the user's eye is too far from the simulation. This is likely with angles of view approaching 130 degrees or more (unless the image is curved and partly surrounds the viewer).

7. Depending on how the picture is presented and on the distance of the user from the picture, the simulation image size may be too large or too small to provide representative views. This means that the simulation image occupies a larger or smaller portion of the observer's total field-of-view than would the same part of the actual scene if the observer were standing at the real viewpoint. The effect is that the project appears to be closer to or farther away from the observer than it should be (Fig. 6-10).

For example, illustrations in reports usually are reproduced at sizes ranging from 4 × 5 inches to 8 1/2 × 11 inches. These tend to be too small for normal reading distances, particularly with wide-angle views. With a typical camera lens (admitting an original field-of-view of approximately 45 degrees), an image 11 inches wide should be viewed at a distance of about 13 inches in order to achieve the correct viewing angle; with the same image presented at 5 inches wide, the eye should be 6 inches from the page. At greater distances from the page, the project appears to be less dominant in the observer's field-of-view than it would really be (Fig. 6-11). Since normal reading distances approximate 18 inches or so, it would appear that most simulations presented on standard-size pages are likely to downplay the apparent scale of projects. The same could be said of most projected images in meeting rooms, where viewing distances often greatly exceed the width of the projected image. Only large boards, mounted on a wall or display so that viewers can approach closely, commonly provide optimum viewing distances.

Figure 6-11. Photosimulation of a corner store and substation, with original field-of-view of 75 degrees (a): at this size, the image should be viewed at a distance of 4 inches from the eye, which is less than focusing distance for many people; the same simulation at this larger size should be viewed at a distance of 6 inches from the eye (b).

Cause of Problems

An unrepresentative set of simulations can arise for a variety of reasons:

1. The number of views to be simulated may be limited by time, budget, space for presentation, and a need to simplify the presentation. Simulating motion, in particular, is costly because of the relatively sophisticated techniques involved and the scarcity of equipment and skilled personnel. Its use is hindered by a lack of awareness that such techniques exist, and a general ignorance of the importance of motion in viewing and judging projects.

2. The selection of viewpoints may be dictated by convenience of access on the ground rather than by their importance to viewers. Commonly, for example, it is difficult to simulate important views from existing freeway overpasses or highway bends because of the lack of safe places from which to take photographs. The creator of a simulation may also be forced to omit viewpoints (such as proposed bridges or inaccessible slopes) that are difficult to reach until the project is built.

3. The preparer of simulations may omit viewpoints that do not afford a view of the project site until planned future changes are enacted (for example, the felling of trees between the project and the viewpoint).

4. Certain simulation media may impose constraints on location of viewpoints. For example, some three-dimensional computer-graphics programs do not permit viewpoints to be located on the surface of the terrain model or structure; scale models with trees and structures represented may not easily afford ground views of a proposed structure from typical viewpoints such as building exits or tree-covered walkways (Fig. 6-12).

5. Preparers who are unskilled in visibility analysis and do not visit the site may fail to identify important views.

6. The selection of viewpoints may be influenced by the distribution of residents or recreation groups that have greater lobbying power or environmental awareness than others. Only the most politically sensitive views may be shown. Official notices to affected landowners may be sent only to those residents close to a project so that residents living a mile away but with clear views of a project may not become aware of a proposed project until it is too late to request simulations.

7. The preparer may deliberately select a viewpoint in order to illustrate a particular aspect of the project (Fig. 6-13) or cast it in a cer-

Figure 6-12. Scale model of a footbridge in a wooded creek setting: the vegetation in the model permits a full view of the bridge only from the creek.

tain light. Views may be chosen to favor a project—for example, by balancing or screening it with existing landscape features—or to make it more obtrusive. Aerial, elevated, or close-up views may be used to aid comprehension of the design, without supplying the information needed to judge it in its typical context. As in the examples of Figures 6-12 and 6-13, the preparer of the simulation may be forced to show an unrepresentative view in order to explain the overall design.

8. The preparer may have too little information on future changes in the project resulting from maintenance, weathering, or tree growth, to attempt to predict their appearance with time.

Figure 6-13. Rendering showing an unusual view of a proposed geothermal power plant, seen from higher elevations that are generally inaccessible to the public.

Solutions

A set of simulations may be considered to be fully representative if it includes

1. All the important viewpoints that give a clear and distinctly different view of the project to significant numbers of people (Plate 15)
2. Views of the project in different conditions that radically affect its appearance (for example, winter and summer, or one year and

fifteen years after construction; see Figs. 2-10, 2-22)
3. Simulation images with adequate field-of-view presented at an image size and viewing distance that recapture the actual viewing relationships and site context

In addition, viewpoints and conditions shown should be identified for the orientation and information of simulation users.

It is, of course, easier to represent a variety of views if motion is included in the simulation by using one of the dynamic techniques. However, the same principle applies in selecting views from continuous routes as in selecting static viewpoints. The view direction, speed of travel, and the route itself should represent typical and important travel sequences that would occur in reality.

PRINCIPLE 2: SIMULATIONS SHOULD BE ACCURATE

Definition

A fully accurate simulation shows a view of the project that is not significantly different in appearance from the real view when seen from the same viewpoint (Fig. 6-14). This is sometimes called the honesty or truthfulness of the picture to real life.

The notion of simulation accuracy, though simple enough in concept, is not always simple to describe or measure. In order to understand what accuracy means in actual cases, it is necessary to explain a few key concepts.

Simulation accuracy can vary in two principal ways: (1) in the subject matter shown, and (2) in the pictorial elements that make up the image.

SUBJECT MATTER. Accuracy in subject matter refers to the presence, absence, or kinds of objects in the scene. A simulation may omit parts of the project or scene that would, in real life, be seen. Alternatively, it may include objects (trees and shrubbery) that do not occur on the site of the completed project. The simulation shown in Figure 6-15, for example, is inaccurate in omitting the houses visible in the photograph of the actual scene.

a

b

Figure 6-14. Transmission line, Solano County, California: In the simulation (a), the power line indicated by the arrow was added to a photograph of the site before construction; the actual view (b) shows how accurate the simulation was in predicting the scale and location of the power line as built.

a

b

Figure 6-15. Cement plant, Davenport, California: rendering of cement plant *(a)*; photograph of actual scene *(b)*.

IMAGE ELEMENTS. Just as a real scene or landscape feature can be described in terms of its various visual elements (see Chapter 3), so any part of a picture or object in an image can be described in terms of the elements of position, scale, shape, color, and detail and texture (Fig. 6-16). These elements can be used to describe any part of the scene in the view or image. For example, in Figure 6-17a the structure is positioned against a distant ridgeline backdrop, extends above the skyline, has a very slender shape, is dark in color, and shows minimal texture or detailed components.

As with subject matter, these image elements may differ between the real view and the simulation. Thus, by comparing the simulation (Fig. 6-17a) with the photograph of the actual view (Fig. 6-17b), we can say that the simulation is accurate in the position and height of the project, but somewhat inaccurate in

- Shape—supports are too slender, and upper structures too small and rectangular
- Color—supports are too dark
- Detail and texture—lacking intricate pattern of latticework and upper structures

With dynamic simulations, it is also important to consider the elements of speed and direction in the motion of objects. Other aspects of accuracy apply equally to static images and animated sequences.

If we were to visit the real project again at another time of day, or in winter, or ten years later, it might well look different; it may have changed considerably with lighting, plant growth, or aging. Consequently, the conditions in which a project's appearance is simulated are

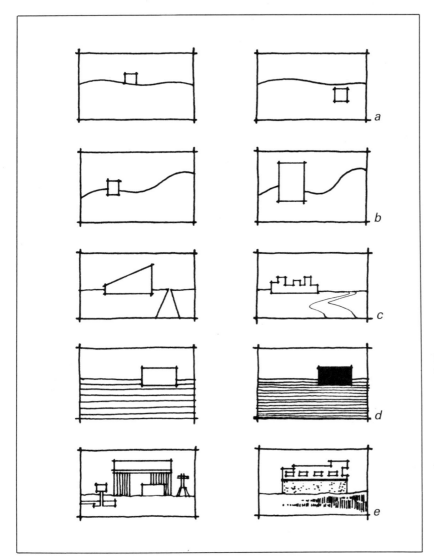

Figure 6-16. Image elements: *position* of the object within the image (high/low, in front/behind, left/right/center, etc.) (*a*); *scale*—size of the object relative to other objects in the image (large/small) (*b*); *shape*—configuration of the object in the image, indicated by its edges, silhouette, and lines (round/square, straight/crooked, regular/irregular, etc.) (*c*); *color*—full color of the object in the image, including its tonal value (light/dark), hue (red/green), and brilliance (bright/dull) (*d*); *detail and texture*—small-scale surface variations and features of the object in the image (simple/complex, rough/smooth, coarse/fine, etc.) (*e*).

Figure 6-17. Ski-jump structure, Lake Placid, New York: sketch of proposed structure *(a)*; photograph of actual scene *(b)*.

important when considering accuracy in the simulation image.

There is some overlap between subject matter and image elements in determining the accuracy of a simulation. For example, the depiction of trees that would not be present on-site will inevitably cause inaccuracies in color, texture, and even the apparent scale of the project in the simulation. There is also a relationship to the representativeness of the simulation: a narrow field-of-view will automatically cause certain subject matter to be omitted from the simulation.

Image elements and subject matter may not be the only criteria of simulation accuracy; a picture may accurately capture the rhythm, atmosphere, or overall feeling of a scene without a one-to-one match of the simulation to the actual view. However, the greater the individual inaccuracies in the simulation, the less likely it is that the general mood will be true to life.

Inaccuracy of image elements and subject matter can also be described in terms of abstraction and distortion.

ABSTRACTION. This means that various elements of the simulation are omitted or simplified, as when color is left out or details and outlines are simplified.

Abstract simulations often look like diagrams or cartoons (Fig. 6-18), and are sometimes called *conceptual simulations* [4] because they show only the basic underlying concepts of an idea or design. Usually this means that they show only the structural elements of a project or scene (position, scale, basic form), and omit surface elements (color, texture and detail). Even position, scale, and form, however, can be generalized or shown in an abstract symbolic fashion (Fig. 6-19).

Precise simulations, on the other hand, show

details and complexities in much the same way as the eye obtains a visual image of the world; precise simulations are often termed *realistic* or *experiential simulations*[4] because they show scenes more as they could be experienced or perceived in real life (Fig. 6-20).

DISTORTION. This means that a simulation, even though it may show the shape, colors, and details of a project, depicts the wrong colors, shape, or details. It is analogous to a distorting mirror that shows a complete image of an object but distorts its appearance.

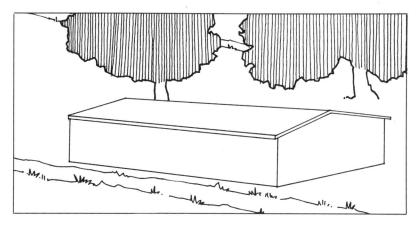

Figure 6-18. Abstract simulation of a building, with surface elements not shown.

Figure 6-19. Examples of simulations showing project location and scale in abstract form.

Figure 6-20. Precise simulation of a building, shown with all image elements (except full color).

Recognition of this form of inaccuracy is important because, even though a simulation is precise and looks realistic, it may still be inaccurate due to distortion. Comparison of the precise simulation in Figure 6-20 with a photograph of the actual building (Fig. 6-21) reveals that the shape and facade details are very different.

Abstract simulations also may contain distortions. Simulations that show only the structural elements in an image may not show the correct position, size, and shape of objects. Moreover, abstract simulations such as that in Figure 6-18 in effect automatically distort the colors of objects (by showing them as white), or the texture and detail of objects (by showing them as plain).

Very simply, therefore, it is possible to categorize simulations of project appearance into four main types as shown in Figure 6-22. These categories are not clear-cut, however, and are useful mainly as a way of thinking about potential inaccuracies. Some simulations are more abstract than others; a simulation can be precisely detailed yet lack all color; another may show the project's shape accurately but depict the wrong hues and texture. It is important to realize that simulation inaccuracy can take many forms. Care should be taken therefore to identify what in the simulation is inaccurate. It should also be remembered, however, that conceptual (abstract) simulations can form a useful stage in the preparation of more precise (experiential) simulations.

Significance

Some forms of inaccuracy may actually improve people's understanding of a project. In particular, abstraction can enhance understanding of some characteristics, such as spatial arrangement. However, the abstract simulation can fail to communicate anything about colors, textures, and important design details. Simulations of building silhouettes may give information on how much blockage of view will occur, but they cannot provide much information on the construction materials, windows, eaves, and overall character of the architecture. Without such information, people find it difficult to judge even the scale of buildings.

Obvious inaccuracies such as these understandably can lead to confusion and distrust among interpreters. Where color schemes are a key issue to communities and agencies, criticisms are to be expected of simulations that fail to show full color (that is, hue and brilliance). Lack of detail and the conspicuous absence of any clutter on-site can invite the criticism that the simulation looks too clean (Fig. 6-23).

Perceived errors in color, shape, detail, and especially scale of the project may also be criticized. In particular, the amount of visual contrast between the proposed project and its surroundings may be disputed. The developer may claim that a consultant's picture exaggerates the proj-

Figure 6-21. Photograph of the actual building simulated in Figures 6-18 and 6-20.

DISTORTION

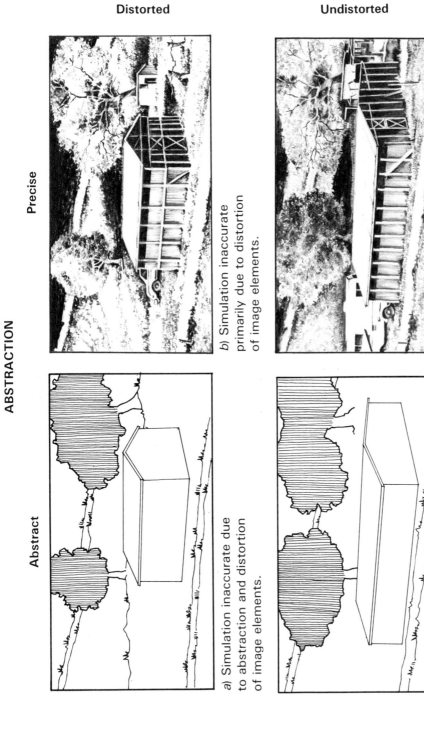

Distorted

Undistorted

Precise

b) Simulation inaccurate primarily due to distortion of image elements.

d) Simulation accurate in most image elements.

e) Actual view.

ABSTRACTION

Abstract

a) Simulation inaccurate due to abstraction and distortion of image elements.

c) Simulation inaccurate primarily due to abstraction of image elements.

Figure 6-22. A classification of simulations according to abstraction and distortion.

Figure 6-23. Sketch of a proposed power plant which elicited predominantly sceptical reactions from environmental professionals in the author's study.

ect's contrast (Fig. 6-24), while opponents of the project may claim the opposite with a designer's rendering.

Overall, therefore, it is clear that perceived inaccuracies are strongly correlated with low credibility in simulations. To what extent, though, is inaccuracy, real or perceived, correlated with bias?

Whether or not their flaws are obvious, inaccurate simulations depict conditions of project appearance that are not or would not be borne out in reality. As a result, such simulations are open to misinterpretation. They can cause decisions to be based on incorrect or incomplete data, potentially leading to poor decisions. The real question is how much and what kind of inaccuracy is needed before significant bias occurs.

The author's study[1] and other research[5,6] suggest that the most accurate simulations are seldom misleading. Whether or not less accurate simulations mislead users seems to depend partly on the kind of inaccuracies present. Based on the author's findings, supported by other applicable research results, the following types of inaccuracy appear to cause bias:

ABSTRACTION. Very abstract simulations, such as simple models and computer-generated line drawings, tend to make the project look worse than actual views (Fig. 6-25 and Plate 16).[7]

Full-color simulations can lead in some cases to more favorable reactions than will similar black-and-white simulations (Plate 17).

Black-and-white line sketches and photomontage massing simulations (the media most commonly used by environmental consultants and some government agencies) tend to make the project's visual impact seem worse to users than do actual views (Fig. 6-26 and Plate 18). Where black-and-white simulations cause unfavorable bias, therefore, full-color simulations may be less misleading.[8,9]

On the other hand, moderately abstract simulations (for example, lacking full color and detail but showing tonal values and all major project components) are generally no more misleading than precise simulations. In other words, *some abstraction is acceptable but too much can cause bias.*

Figure 6-24. Computer graphics have been criticized by wind-resource developers as exaggerating the visual impact of wind-turbine facilities due to color contrasts of black ink on white paper. © Dynamic Graphics, Inc.

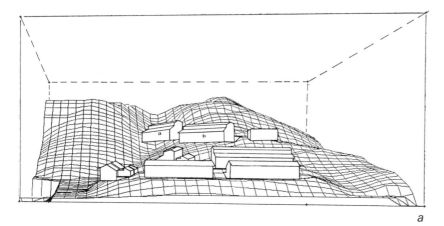

a

b

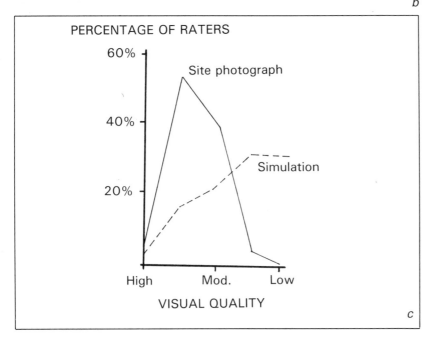

PERCENTAGE OF RATERS

Site photograph

Simulation

VISUAL QUALITY

High   Mod.   Low

c

Figure 6-25. Housing project in Marin County, California: computer graphic of proposed project *(a);* photograph of actual view of the same project *(b);* variations in visual quality ratings of the two scenes *(c)* (*Source:* S. Sheppard 1982).

a

b

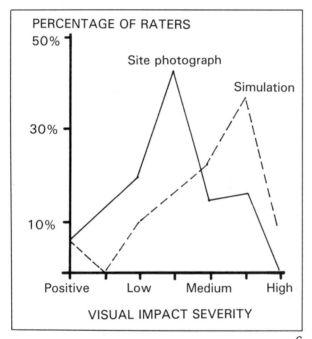

c

Figure 6-26. Residential project, Marin County, California: black-and-white photomontage of project *(a)*; photograph of actual view *(b)*; variations in visual-impact ratings of the two scenes *(c)* (*Source:* S. Sheppard 1982).

DISTORTION IN CONTRAST BETWEEN PROJECT AND SETTING. Simulations that exaggerate the prominence of a project and increase its visual contrast in relation to the surroundings (for example, in color or scale) can lead to less favorable judgments of visual impact (Fig. 6-27 and Plate 19). On the other hand, while the sketch of the structure shown in Fig. 6-17*a* has inaccuracies in proportion and detail, the basic shape, scale, and setting are shown correctly, and visual-impact ratings were similar in both the simulation and the actual view.[1]

RENDERING STYLE. This is really a form of abstraction, in terms of stylistic departure from realism. In comparison with other kinds of simulation used on the same project, artists' renderings tend to make the scene more attractive. Research suggests that in some cases, they may make the scene look somewhat better than it does in reality, even when the rendering style is relatively neutral and restrained (Fig. 6-28).

The author found that virtually all cases of bias in favor of the project involved renderings by professional illustrators and project designers. Some drawings turned out to be biased against the project, however, while many, including those that were moderately abstract, turned out to be quite unbiased. Lay people may, nonetheless, be more misled by renderings than would professional users such as those participating in the author's study.

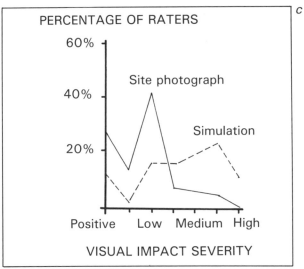

PERCENTAGE OF RATERS

VISUAL IMPACT SEVERITY

Figure 6-27. Bridge, near Walnut Creek, California: model of white bridge *(a)*; photograph of actual bridge with less contrasting treatment *(b)*; variations in visual impact ratings of the two scenes *(c)* (*Source:* S. Sheppard 1982).

a

b

Figure 6-28. Highway bridge near Napa, California: rendering of proposed highway bridge (*a*); photograph of actual view of project (*b*).

Problems in Practice

Major discrepancies between simulations and real views appear to be the rule rather than the exception. Overall accuracy as measured by the author in his survey of simulations averaged only 57 percent of the total accuracy possible in a two-dimensional image.* Inaccuracies attributable to the original simulation image are common and affect both subject matter and image elements. Examples are illustrated in the following section.

INACCURACY IN SUBJECT MATTER

- Omission of clutter—subsidiary parts of the project and associated development such as cut-and-fill slopes, fencing, discarded material, on-site equipment, utilities, and smoke plumes (Fig. 6-29).
- Omission of surrounding context within the field-of-view, for example, adjoining highways, buildings, utility lines, and distant ridgelines or backdrops (Fig. 6-30).
- Showing people, cars, yachts, or other dynamic and visually interesting objects in the wrong places or in greater numbers than they normally would occur (Plate 20).[10] (Wood et al. conducted an interesting analysis of the unrepresentative types of people shown in architectural renderings.)[11]
- Including grass, shrubs, and trees that would not actually be present, particularly in the foreground or framing the view (Fig. 6-31).

INACCURACY IN IMAGE ELEMENTS. Inaccuracies in the color, tonal value, shape, and detail and texture of the project and its contrast with setting are commonplace. Both distortion and abstraction of the image occur frequently.

*See Appendix D for a description of methods used in the study.

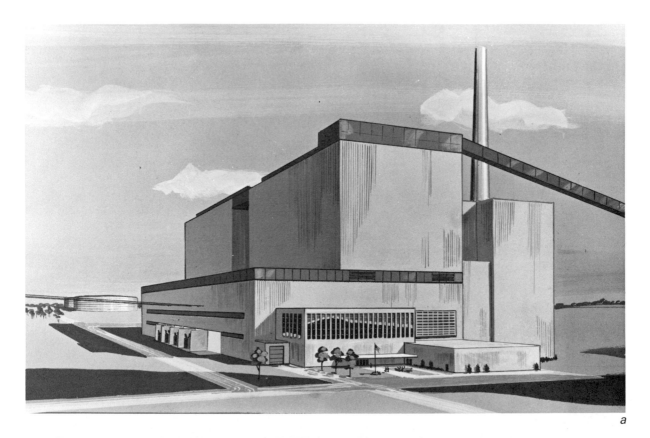

a

b

Figure 6-29. Power plant near Kenosha, Wisconsin: simulation of power plant (*a*); photograph of real project, showing much more clutter (*b*).

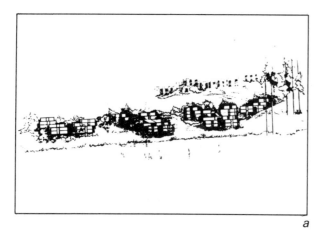

a   *b*

Figure 6-30. Housing project in Marin County, California: simulation of project (*a*); photograph of real project, revealing more context including freeway and commercial buildings (*b*).

a   *b*

Figure 6-31. Fountain in a Denver park: simulation of proposed design (*a*); photograph of real project, showing different trees in the foreground (*b*).

- Many simulations (50 percent in the author's survey) show distortion in the position, scale, and shape of the project (Fig. 6-32).

- Many simulations (66 percent in the author's survey) show incorrect tonal values (patterns of dark and light) or lack tonal values (Fig. 6-33).

- Most simulations (over two-thirds in the author's survey) lack full color, and even those that originally are created in color usually are reproduced in black and white (see Plate 17).

- Of those simulations having full color, most (about 75 percent in the author's survey) show distinctly different colors from those that would typically be seen on-site (Plate 21).

- Many simulations (about 60 percent in the author's survey) either lack detail and texture (see Fig. 3-12) or show different details and textures.

Whether or not the original simulation is accurate, problems in presentation or public display for public review also occur (see also Principle 3: Simulations Should Be Clear). These primarily affect the abstraction and distortion of image elements, as for example when the colors of a re-photographed simulation shift, or detail is lost through the reproduction process. It is very common for environmental impact reports to contain black-and-white photocopies of original simulations, resulting in considerable loss of potentially important information. Where images are projected at a much larger size than anticipated, the accuracy can break down, as when photographs of a part of a larger simulation are blown up to a large size, exposing any minor flaw or visual inconsistency for all to see.

a

b

Figure 6-32. Reservoir in Marin County, California: simulation of project (*a*); photograph of real project, showing different configuration of the dam (*b*).

Figure 6-33. Photomontage of proposed housing project, with no tonal values shown in the buildings.

Causes of Problems

Inaccuracies in simulations are not always avoidable or necessarily undesirable as, for example, when it is important to simplify an image in order to help people understand the project. Inaccuracies can occur for a variety of reasons:

LIMITATIONS OF SIMULATION MEDIA. Some types of simulation, for example, photosimulations, renderings, and high-resolution solid-color computer graphics, may permit more precision and a wider range of colors, detail, and texture than do more limited media (Fig. 6-34 and Plate 22). The choice of simulation medium may be dictated by cost, time constraints, reproduction needs, availability of materials, equipment, and skills, familiarity with the medium, and other factors. Many of the newest technologies in electronic and computer-graphic simulation are not yet widely known or are not yet compatible with

the equipment and software that users may already have.

PROJECT INFORMATION. The information available to the preparer of a simulation may be preliminary, overly general, incomplete, or conflicting. In such cases, preparers must use guesswork, make further inquiries, or simply omit features of the project about which they are uncertain.

The information used in preparing simulations may also be incorrect due to errors in the project design, in the reproduction of data, and in the basic site data. The accuracy of computer-generated perspectives, for example, is highly dependent upon the accuracy of topographic maps or digital data. Another source of inaccuracy is a change in the project plan that the preparer was not aware of at the time the simulation was created. It is common for changes in plan to be made after the simulation has been prepared.

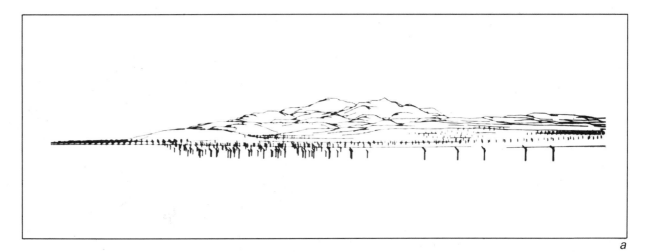

Figure 6-34. Simulation of wind turbines with a computer-graphic software program (*a*), able to show only lines (© Dynamic Graphics, Inc); simulation of wind turbines by photo retouching (*b*), a medium capable of showing all image elements except motion.

These changes may result from the use of simulations in the project-review process. The author's survey, however, found few documented cases (less than 5 percent) where discrepancies in appearance between simulation and reality could be attributed to mitigation measures demanded after people had seen the simulations (see Fig. 6-27, showing the subdued color scheme of a footbridge [*b*], which was decided upon after local residents had requested a structure with less visual impact than the white bridge shown in the simulation [*a*]).

Another cause of inaccuracy is the failure to take into account future changes in land use surrounding the project site, even though they might influence the view of the project considerably (Fig. 6-35).

EXPERIENCE OF PREPARER. Some people are more familiar with and skilled in making simulations than others. It is not uncommon for technical illustrators without training in perspective drawing, or relatively untrained staff members of environmental consulting firms, to be given the job of "doing simulations" for a report. Substantial mistakes can result. Experience helps in visualizing and depicting complex or subtle relationships in the landscape. Nonetheless, experienced preparers of simulations may develop distinct techniques, artistic styles, and graphic symbols, which can reduce accuracy, suggest visual and aesthetic effects that may not occur in reality, or obscure important characteristics of the project. Such stylistic inaccuracies are common because designers and artists are taught to

Figure 6-35. Simulation of housing project (*a*); photograph (*b*) reveals extensive development in the foreground, with project still under construction beyond.

express themselves and make their own work distinctive (Fig. 6-36).

Use of automated or highly technical simulation media such as computer graphics does not eliminate the risk of inaccuracy through operator error. Use of computer personnel who do not have a good understanding of spatial and perceptual elements, or use of environmental professionals who do not have a good understanding of the software and data limits, can easily lead to errors and inaccuracies. In practice, it is something of an art to provide computer perspectives that can be sized precisely and overlaid to match photographs correctly.

SHORTCUTS AND GUESSWORK. Even experienced preparers of simulations may be tempted to speed up the process or avoid extra work by

guessing rather than calculating or researching details that affect accuracy. Guesswork is induced by the pressure of deadlines and an overconfidence in one's own abilities and eye for perspective. There is no real disincentive against guesswork so long as (1) no one is likely to ask for step-by-step documentation of how the simulation was prepared, and (2) no one is going to check the accuracy of the simulation against the real thing if the project is built.

Guesswork is especially likely to cause inaccuracies when used by inexperienced preparers or by experts who are interpreting from plans and photographs without visiting the site.

INADEQUATE PLANNING AND FIELD PROCEDURES. Failure to take or use appropriate tools in fieldwork can limit accuracy considerably. Ex-

Figure 6-36. Examples of artistic styles affecting simulated appearance of projects.

amples include neglecting to bring scale markers to establish a reference height or detailed maps to record the viewpoint carefully, and failing to document photographs taken.

DELIBERATE ATTEMPTS AT BIAS. The preparer of the simulation may deliberately attempt to exaggerate the positive qualities of a project and thus bias the opinions of those judging it in favor of

the proposal (Fig. 6-37). Conversely, opponents of the project may attempt to persuade others by exaggerating negative qualities. To these ends, objects in the scene may be selectively omitted or added and their appearance altered in some way. Urban projects that would, if successful, promote activity and bustle may be simulated with bright colors, many animated objects, and numerous people to give a lively, fresh, exciting

Figure 6-37. The same building shown by the same artist but in two different styles.

appearance. The composition of the view may be manipulated to frame, balance, or highlight the project artificially. A looser, softer artistic style or simulation medium may be chosen over a more precise and realistic technique where project proponents fear a negative reaction to a design.

Deliberate distortions such as these can take many forms and can be very subtle indeed. They are a common cause of inaccuracy in simulations prepared by designers and professional illustrators whose interests are best served by making the project look as attractive, acceptable, or salable as possible (see Plate 20).

NEED TO EXPLAIN PROJECTS.   There may be a legitimate need for special presentations to illustrate or explain particularly complex or unfamiliar aspects of the project design, such as the overall concept or individual design details. Abstract or selective pictures may be used for this purpose. The inaccuracies entailed may, however, be open to misinterpretation if they are not balanced by additional simulations showing expected views as they would be seen in reality.

Solutions

A simulation may be considered to be accurate if it

- contains all parts of the project and surroundings that would be visible in that view
- illustrates the project and surroundings in approximately the position, scale, shape, color, and important detail they would have in that view in reality
- uses techniques that have been tested and their accuracy verified (see Principle 5: Simulations Should Be Defensible)

PRINCIPLE 3: SIMULATIONS SHOULD BE CLEAR

Definition

A simulation has clarity if the visual content of the image is clearly and unambiguously expressed, is presented without loss of detail, contrast, or sharpness, and is free of distracting or competing elements.

Problems of visual clarity become evident in a number of ways, including

- overstylized images
- overly detailed images
- poorly reproduced images (fuzzy, blurred, grainy, dark, uneven, or washed-out pictures)
- flicker, blur, interference, poor lighting, and other factors in presentation of simulations
- too large or too small an image
- distracting labels, special effects, borders, or formats

Significance

If a simulation is visually unclear, it fails to communicate the correct information or risks the wrong interpretation. It thus can lead to confusion and bias, as well as to a lack of credibility. An original simulation image that is fully accurate and representative can still result in these problems if its clarity is reduced by the reproduction or presentation process. Details of architecture or signage, for example, can be very important in forming people's impressions of a project or expressing its meaning; when a detailed simulation becomes boiled down to a small photocopy in a report for mass distribution, much of this important information can be lost (Plate 23). This situation leads to the same consequences as when a simulation is intentionally produced in an abstract form (see Principle 2).

On the other hand, it is possible for a simulation to be too clear, in other words, to make a point too forcefully. For example, the use of symbols or arrows to identify components in a scene may artificially draw attention to those features (Fig. 6-38). Other graphic devices may equally distract attention away from the important features and thus downplay positive or negative design features.

Problems in Practice

As has been noted, most environmental reports contain black-and-white reproductions of original simulations, and after two or three generations of photocopying, their visual clarity is often very low. Moreover, in the author's survey, some 8 percent of the criticisms leveled at simulations by environmental professionals referred to their be-

Figure 6-38. Photomontages with symbols used to label proposed high-rise buildings in views from the Washington Mall, D.C.

ing too sketchy, stylized, or symbol-ridden (Fig. 6-39).[1]

The advent of new simulation technologies does not automatically reduce this problem. The more widely available video image-processing techniques for use with personal computers typically are limited in resolution to approximately 500 to 600 lines on the screen; this is insufficient for clear depiction of small detail, and, depending on the printing process, the result can be decidedly unclear hard copy (Plate 24). New technologies like this can run the additional risk of failing to meet people's expectations of image quality based on more traditional media.

More conventional wire-frame computer graphics can also become visually confusing (Fig. 6-40), particularly when hidden lines are not removed; these are lines or edges of objects that would be behind other solid objects and should therefore be invisible, but which are shown in the simulation as though the objects in front were transparent. The increasing use of CADD systems may increase the incidence of such simulations, although the capability of hidden-line removal is becoming more of a standard feature in such programs.

Figure 6-39. Simulation of water pumping facility which was considered "too sketchy" by study participants.

Figure 6-40. Example of computer graphic without hidden-line removal.

Causes of Problems

Insufficient simulation clarity of the types discussed is generally caused by one or more of the following:

- Lack of knowledge or attention on the part of presenters. Reports and presentations often are prepared by people who are not familiar with graphic reproduction needs, and who were not involved in the preparation of the simulation itself.
- Inadequate planning. Failure to plan for quality assurance and suitable reproduction or display usually leads to poor presentations. Simulations that are not created with a view to eventual reproduction or use in other formats are likely to suffer loss of clarity when presented.
- Restricted budgets, allowing only the cheapest and lowest quality forms of reproduction, and often resulting in smaller images.
- Equipment limitations. The medium of video, for example, varies in quality depending on the type of monitor, quality of tape, signal degradation due to duplication of tapes, size of the monitor in relation to the number of people watching, and so on. Problems of focus, poor lighting, and improper viewing angle commonly bedevil slide presentations, wall displays, and overhead projection.

- Preparer's style or lack of skill, leading to overly stylized or "sketchy" simulations.
- Selection of a medium inappropriate to the audience. Visual clarity is to some extent relative; it depends upon the user's familiarity in interpreting symbols or indistinct images, much as an expert radiologist can detect vital information from a CAT scan that looks like a meaningless jumble of colors to the patient. Thus, as with abstract simulations, trained engineers or designers who routinely work with complex computer graphics or indistinct video images may be able to understand simulations that the lay person finds totally unclear.

Solutions

Problems of clarity are easier to avoid than those of unrepresentative or inaccurate simulations. It requires planning so that both the presentation medium and type of audience are considered before the simulations are prepared. The simulation technique can then be fitted to the appropriate budget and vice versa. Specifications can be developed to preserve the visual clarity of images when reproduced.

Potentially distracting or confusing features in a simulation can be screened out prior to any public showing. If doubt remains on the issue of clarity, the presentation of the simulation can be tested on a small scale or in various versions, prior to mass production or public display in its final form.

PRINCIPLE 4: SIMULATIONS SHOULD BE INTERESTING

Definition

A simulation or set of simulations is sufficiently interesting if it holds the viewers' attention throughout the presentation period and involves them in the issue at hand. This is what Appleyard describes as "engaging the viewer."[4] Interest can be derived from the simulations themselves and from the way they are presented. It varies with the content of the simulations, their complexity, novelty, and dynamism, and also the pacing of the presentation.

Significance

Simulations must be able to hold peoples' attention if their message is to be communicated. Once the audience becomes bored, they will turn off, literally or in effect. Thus they may miss important information and make decisions based on initial impressions or on their instincts.

A simulation presentation that is too interesting or engaging, however, becomes a form of entertainment that can be counterproductive. The audience may become so involved, or so fascinated by the technique, that they lose sight of the real issues or are left with a favorable impression that may be erroneously transferred to the project. Alternatively, some users may be put off by presentations that are too slick or high-tech, feeling them to be more like a public-relations gimmick or advertising pitch than an information tool.

Problems in Practice

Studies to document the level of interest in simulations do not appear to have been conducted, but examples in practice suggest trends. In general, simulations presenting visual information stand out from the mass of verbal or written information that often accompanies them; these therefore capture the most interest and attention, at least in the short term. Boredom or uninvolvement usually sets in only under the following conditions:

- Simulations are presented in large numbers
- Presentation occurs over a protracted period in which the viewer has too long to study each image
- Simulations are repeated
- Simulations are similar in content and appear repetitive

These conditions usually occur only in specialized research or workshop conditions where an environmental or aesthetic issue is being studied in some depth. In these instances, the concerns of the participants affected by the issue may counterbalance the lack of interest or diversity in presentations. It is possible, however, that the general public's attention span limits the number of simulations (viewpoints and/or project alternatives simulated) that can be presented effectively.

The problem of overly interesting or entertaining simulations has not yet become widespread, although it is likely to occur more frequently as animated computer graphics and video presentations become more commonplace. It is, however, quite common for people to express fascination with the realism of well-prepared photosimulations or the ''magic'' of computer graphics, and the effect of such feelings on decision-making is not well understood.

Causes of Problems

The problem of boredom is most likely to occur where there is the necessity of investigating visual issues in considerable detail in response to specific government policies or interest-group concerns; people not associated with those concerns may well lose interest at an early stage. The problem is most acute where viewers are obliged to sit through a presentation, as in a public hearing, rather than being allowed to exercise free choice as in reviewing an environmental report or wall displays. Boredom results generally from the failure of the presenters to predict accurately how long a presentation will take or how much interest people will have in the simulations. Usually this is caused by inexperience on the part of the presenters or miscalculations on the makeup of the audience; it is often impossible to predict who will turn up at the public meetings where simulations are being used.

There are also differences in people's expectations for various media. Video and television are hard to resist when turned on, but, by the same token, people may be far less tolerant of slow pacing with this medium than with slides or static images where they do not expect continual change in the viewing sequence.

Entertaining simulations can be a result of deliberate attempts to please and involve the audience, or of failure to understand how other people will react to techniques that may be unfamiliar or reminiscent of a public-relations tool. Developers will sometimes hire audiovisual production experts who are trained to use special effects and other eye-catching tricks of the trade to promote a client, but who lack a full understanding of the environmental issues and public sensibilities at the heart of conflicts over proposed projects.

Solutions

Presentations containing simulations should be kept brief enough to avoid boring most people. If some sectors of the audience wish to dwell on simulation issues, they should be given opportunities that do not require the attention of the entire group and permit more choice in the duration or number of showings. Similarly, in reports, multiple simulations showing similar conditions may best be placed in an appendix if they are likely to exhaust the reader's attention in the body of the report.

With some of the more realistic or dynamic simulation techniques, it may not be possible to avoid the fascination that people inherently experience, at least until they are so familiar with the technique that they cease to wonder about how it is done. Blatantly entertaining simulations should, however, be screened out by relatively experienced people, such as planning staff.

In all cases where doubt exists, pretesting on a formal or informal basis with a few people (including individuals representing the lay person) can determine appropriate levels of interest and optimal duration of presentations.

PRINCIPLE 5: SIMULATIONS SHOULD BE DEFENSIBLE

Definition

A simulation is defensible when it is seen to be legitimate; that is, when evidence is presented along with the simulation to show how it was produced and to what extent it is accurate and representative. Legitimacy means establishing the authenticity of products and process, and providing some accountability for future problems or disputes.

Significance

Simulations presented without such evidence are vulnerable to attack by people who wish to discredit them or the studies accompanying them, and by those who simply do not believe what they are shown. In other words, without proof that a simulation is correct, its credibility is at risk. Planners often complain that they do not know whether to believe a simulation; perfectly good simulations may, therefore, be ignored and poor land-use or design decisions may result. In legal cases, lack of documented evidence on the validity of simulations can be a fatal flaw to the argument.

Where the simulation process is documented and demonstrated, arguments over correctness can be resolved and attention can be focused on the more important project issues, such as design quality or visual impacts. If the documentation reveals that the simulation methods are inaccurate or questionable, credibility will be lost, but decisions can at least be based on other more reliable information or on improved simulations.

Lack of accountability for simulations can have potentially serious implications for the preparer of simulations. If, after a simulation is prepared, the project design is changed and the modified project is built, accusations may begin to fly that the simulation did not accurately portray the project. Without documentation, the preparer is essentially unprotected and may not be able to shift the responsibility (and any liability) onto the proper party. A documented defensible process also means that the preparer could, if necessary, turn over his or her information to other preparers and expect them to prepare a similar simulation; the simulation would be repeatable and reliable. If two preparers produce very different simulations of the same project, one of them must be wrong. Such things do happen (Fig. 6-41). Without proof of accuracy, it can be impossible to convince anyone that it is the other person's simulation that is wrong.

Problems in Practice

Surprisingly few simulations are presented with supporting evidence of their legitimacy. The aspect of legitimacy that is referred to most commonly is the selection of viewpoints to be simulated. This is often discussed in reports and verbal presentations, although by no means consistently. The author has noted complaints from planners regarding the poor documentation of viewpoints used and viewing conditions shown.

a   *b*

Figure 6-41. Different simulations of the same project prepared by two different people.

Occasionally, brief information is given on the media and techniques used, but graphics that display intermediate stages in the preparation of simulations, or show how the scale of the project was verified, rarely are presented. Less than 10 percent of the simulations surveyed by the author were accompanied by any sort of visual evidence supporting their accuracy; those that did provide such evidence were photosimulations accompanied by computer perspectives used to scale and locate the project correctly (Fig. 6-42).

Computer-generated perspectives, if they are understandable, seem to be accepted readily by lay people as objective and accurate tools in support of final, detailed simulations. This kind of evidence appears to be becoming more common on controversial projects and in legal cases involving aesthetics. The author, while on the witness stand, has even had perspective-calculations sheets taken as court evidence. Photographs of on-site scale markers, such as survey poles at the corners of a proposed building (Fig. 6-43), also are used occasionally to verify more complete simulations showing the final design.

Causes of Problems

The lack of documented legitimacy in simulation probably is due to the low expectations of users and the complacency of preparers. Despite the rising tide of public and agency concern over aesthetics, most illustrators and planners still see simulation as a final product rather than as a process to aid decision-making. There is hardly ever any formal requirement (outside the courtroom) to provide proof of legitimacy or to justify the methods used. In part, this may be due to the technical nature of some simulation techniques, which can make documentation laborious to compile and, later, to review. Also, many planners may doubt their own ability to evaluate the accuracy of simulations, even with all the information at hand. Even if the right questions were to be asked, the potential for the preparer to blind the evaluator with facts and details is substantial.

A major contributing cause of this problem is that many simulations, especially renderings and

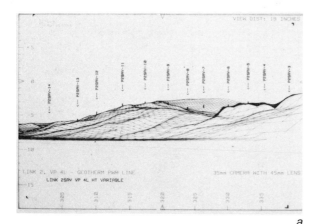

a

abstract photomontages, are prepared without a solid procedure. When preparers are using guesswork and ad hoc methods, there may be very little to document, and no incentive or precedent for documentation. This situation is most likely to occur in nonspecialized firms and agencies where relatively inexperienced graphics or environmental staff may be left to prepare simulations as best they can, by a process of trial and error.

b

c

Figure 6-42. Computer perspectives (*a,b*) used to validate photosimulations (*c*) of a proposed power-line project.

Figure 6-43. Mock-up of proposed building.

There may be other reasons for not demonstrating legitimacy. Time and budget may not permit the display of additional supporting graphics, for example. Another reason might be that intermediate or preliminary simulations, although helpful to the preparer, would be visually confusing or unconvincing to lay people.

Solutions

The authenticity of simulations can be established by providing the following information:

- Description of major data sources, assumptions, uncertainties, and tolerances or margins of error in preparing simulations
- Rationale for selecting viewpoints and viewing concerns
- Graphic evidence supporting the accuracy of the simulation and showing the steps in calculating or generating perspectives and preparing final simulations

This information may not need to be presented with the simulation, but it can be on file or to hand in case questions arise. Merely mentioning that it exists may be helpful in establishing credibility and avoiding the need to rebut accusations or answer questions.

If government agencies or public groups were to require this sort of information as a matter of routine, the quality of simulations would probably improve, and the need to prove the legitimacy of simulations might actually become less urgent.

If simulations are representative, accurate, clear, interesting, and defensible, they are likely to fulfill the fundamental objectives of being understandable, credible, and fair. However, as pointed out in Chapter 5, external factors, such as the political context, mood of the audience, style of the presenter, quality of accompanying environmental studies, and intrinsic popularity or unpopularity of certain types of projects, can all compromise the value of even a perfect simulation. In such situations, adherence to simulation principles can sometimes minimize the damage that external factors may cause; moreover, the more difficult the situation, the more important it is to follow these principles if rational decisions on visual and design issues are to be made.

REFERENCES

1. Sheppard, S. R. J. 1982. ''Landscape portrayals: their use, accuracy, and validity in simulating proposed landscape changes.'' Ph.D. diss., University of California, Berkeley.

2. Blair, W. G. E., I. Robertson, and D. Dingfield. 1982. ''The visual effects of port redevelopment alternatives.'' *Coastal Zone Management Journal* 9(3/4):323–50.

3. Environmental Simulation Laboratory, U.C. Berkeley. Undated. ''The Changing Suburb.'' Unpublished videotape. College of Environmental Design, University of California, Berkeley.

4. Appleyard, D. 1977. ''Understanding professional media.'' In *Human Behavior and Environment,* Vol. 1, ed. Altman and Wohlwill, New York: Plenum Press, pp. 43–88.

5. Wood, W. 1972. ''An analysis of simulation media.'' Master's thesis, University of British Columbia, Vancouver.

6. Craik, K. H., D. Appleyard, and G. E. McKechnie. 1980. *Impressions of a Place: Effects of Media and Familiarity among Environmental Professionals.* Research Technical Report. Berkeley, Calif.: Institute of Personality Assessment and Research, University of California.

7. Sims, W. R. 1974. ''Iconic simulations: an evaluation of their effectiveness as techniques for simulating environmental experience along cognitive, affective, and behavioral dimensions.'' Ph.D. diss., Massachusetts Institute of Technology, Cambridge, Mass.

8. Schomaker, J. H. 1978. ''Measurement of preferences for proposed landscape modifications.'' *Landscape Research* 3(3):5–8.

9. Anderson, J. M. 1970. ''A television aid to design presentation.'' *Architectural Research and Training* 1(2):20–24.

10. Cooper Marcus, C. 1986. *Housing as if People Mattered.* Berkeley, Calif.: University of California Press.

11. Wood, E. W., Jr., S. Brower, and M. W. Latimer. 1966. ''Planners' people.'' *Journal of the American Institute of Planners* 32(4):228–34.

Chapter 7

PRACTICAL GUIDELINES

How can the principles described in the last chapter be applied in practice? How can the many potential problems in simulation use be prevented or detected? This chapter makes practical recommendations for those who prepare or interpret simulations. It is not a step-by-step instruction manual for specific simulation media. Rather, it provides basic recommendations that apply generally both to the range of conventional static simulations and to newer techniques such as advanced computer graphics, video image processing, and animation.

The preceding chapter described typical problems and potential solutions that influence the quality of simulations in terms of comprehension, credibility, and bias. These are the fundamental requirements of simulation in project planning. There are, however, in addition, other functional requirements that are important in the day-to-day practicalities of using simulations.

Typical questions asked when simulations are being considered include

- How quickly can we get them?
- How much will they cost?
- Can we do them in-house or should we hire a specialist?

- What equipment or computer software will we need?
- How easy is it to reproduce them?
- In what form should we present them?

Functional considerations therefore include

- cost
- flexibility of application
- ease of preparation
- speed of preparation
- accessibility/portability/ease of presentation
- durability and storage

The means of simulation is often chosen on the basis of these functional considerations rather than on the potential for validity, fairness, and effectiveness of the final simulation. The impact on simulation quality can be major. At the same time, simulations need to work well in the real world, under real constraints, and so, in every case, a compromise must be reached between ideal results and functional constraints.

This chapter attempts to translate simulation principles into practical solutions that respond to the fundamental questions of simulation use; these solutions need to be easy to implement under normal circumstances and responsive to the more typical questions of logistics. The important point is that the logistical questions are not the only questions that need to be asked when contemplating the use of simulations.

The process for using simulations has been outlined in Chapter 5, Figure 5-1. This records the series of decisions and tasks that typically must be carried out in practice when simulations are planned, produced, presented, and interpreted. In this chapter, the author proposed a significantly modified and improved process, as shown in Figure 7-1. Considerable emphasis is placed on the need to plan the simulation effort carefully, rather than assuming that any simulation will be sufficient. However, the major change recommended in this process is that an additional element, *simulation appraisal,* should be included, at two different stages:

1. After simulations have been prepared and before they are presented to the public or other audience, they should be reviewed or appraised by an appropriate person or agency in order to screen for possible problems.
2. After the project is built, the simulations should be reappraised by comparing them with the project. This, more than anything else, would demonstrate where simulations succeed or fail.

Although this process may, at first glance, seem rather involved, in fact, most of the steps or decisions are an inevitable part of producing simulations, and always have been. Furthermore, many of the decisions can be made quickly and simply. The point of delineating each part of the process is to show that preparers have a choice at every stage, and should not automatically follow a given path without thinking about the consequences. As an aid in giving weight to the most appropriate aspects of a simulation exercise, Table 7-1 shows which principles from Chapter 6 are particularly critical for the various roles or applications of simulation.

The overall process shown in Figure 7-1 will be used to structure the guidelines given in this chapter. The first two sections, on planning and preparing simulations, are primarily for people who intend to produce simulations themselves or take responsibility for having them produced; there are recommendations for both experienced and inexperienced preparers. The next section describes how simulations should be presented, and is for anyone who presents his or her own or someone else's simulations. The fourth section describes how to appraise simulations (prior to project construction); it is intended mainly for project reviewers who routinely use and interpret other people's simulations and need to know how good they are. However, it also serves as a check for preparers who wish to carry out quality

TABLE 7-1.   CRITICAL SIMULATION PROPERTIES FOR DIFFERENT APPLICATIONS

Application of Simulation in Project Planning	Simulation Properties				
	Representativeness	Accuracy	Visual Clarity	Interest	Legitimacy
Design/internal planning	■	■ *			
General orientation		■ *	■	■	
Environmental assessment	■	■			■
Mitigation planning	■	■ *			
Agency/legal decision-making	■	■	■	■	■
Construction guides		■ *	■		
Monitoring	■	■	■		

*Accuracy may be important only for those aspects of the scene that are under consideration.

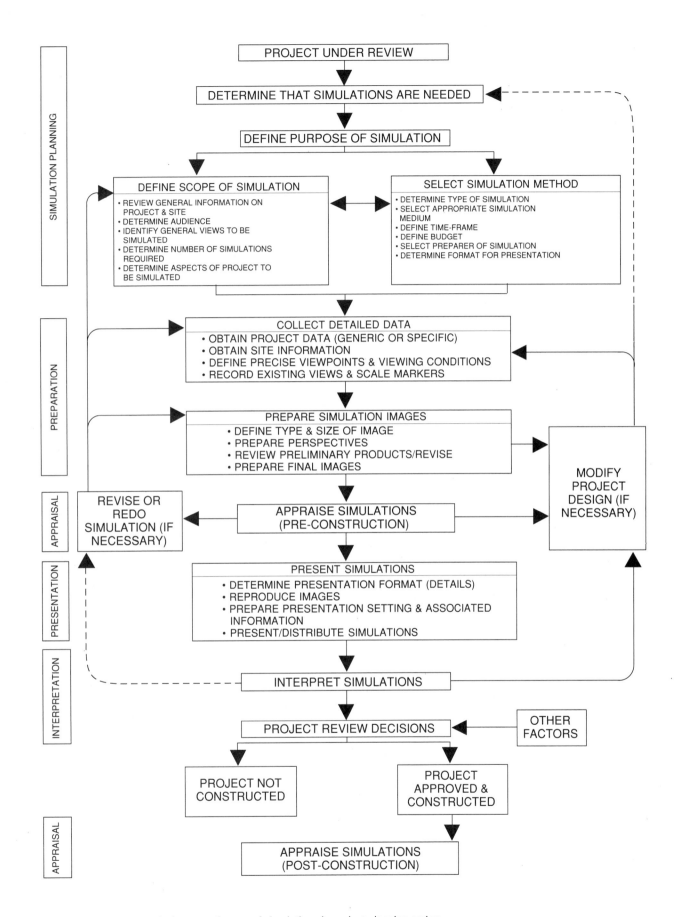

Figure 7-1. Recommended process for use of simulations in project planning and review.

control on their own simulations. The final section describes how to conduct postconstruction appraisal of simulations, as part of the postconstruction evaluation of projects. Although this would be very valuable for preparers of simulations, it is primarily of use to regulatory agencies responsible for monitoring projects.

Note that, in the actual order of the stages in this process, preconstruction appraisal should precede presentation, so that potential problems can be remedied before the public or decision-makers see the simulations. For simplicity's sake in the text, the presentation stage is described after preparation and before preconstruction appraisal, in recognition that simulation preparers often present their own work, and that the intended presentation format should also be appraised by the reviewer.

Appendix A provides more details of specific techniques useful in preparing or appraising simulations. Again, these techniques are applicable to a variety of media.

GUIDELINES FOR SIMULATION PLANNING

Good simulations result from careful planning, not by chance, artistry, or formulas. Before any graphics are produced, an initial analysis is needed to determine what needs to be shown in the simulation and how the simulation is to be presented and used.

Define the Purpose of Simulation

The first step is to define the purpose or application of the simulation. Decide which of the following purposes the simulations need to fulfill (see Chapter 2 for more information on simulation applications).

- To help the project design team to develop, test, and improve their designs
- To explain the project to people who are unfamiliar with it
- To help those responsible to predict and assess future environmental impacts due to the project
- To help identify, develop, and test potential

mitigation measures to reduce adverse impacts
- To document and illustrate the results of environmental studies for the benefit of those seeking to verify the findings in regulatory or legal decisions
- To assist the construction of projects as planned
- To provide a standard against which the postconstruction performance of the project can be judged

These applications can require different types of simulation (see below). Often a simulation needs to satisfy more than a single purpose. Whatever the purpose, the fundamental objectives of comprehension, credibility, and fairness still apply. Answering this first basic question sets the context for resolving the many more detailed questions on scope and technique.

Next, identify a more specific set of aims. For example, a simulation may be needed to show a group of concerned homeowners what the project would look like from their backyards; to provide project engineers with a better understanding of how certain design details could affect overall appearance; or to respond to specific wording on design control in a county ordinance or scenic-area management plan. At this stage, you will be tempted to make specific decisions about the simulations. In order to make better decisions based on a comprehensive review of important issues, you need to define the scope of the simulation and select the appropriate techniques. These steps need to be considered together in arriving at an appropriate simulation plan.

Define the Scope of Simulation

This task defines, in general, what will be shown (that is, the content of the simulation).

OBTAIN GENERAL INFORMATION. Consider the project, site, and current stage in the project approval process:

- general site and/or regional maps
- project description overview
- any relevant environmental studies on the project
- photographs of the site area or project type

- environmental or design regulations to be complied with

REVIEW THE NATURE OF THE PROJECT. Different project types tend to call for different approaches:

- Is the project large in scale (like a factory) or small (like a single-family home)?
- Is it associated with a single site, alternative sites, or a linear corridor (such as a highway or pipeline)?
- Is it controversial or generally well accepted?
- Is it unusual or typical of many other projects in the area?
- Is it complex in its design or the phasing of construction?
- Has any kind of visual analysis been prepared for this project or site already?

REVIEW THE SITE CONDITIONS

- Is the site particularly scenic, highly visible, or otherwise visually sensitive?
- Is the site covered by regulations or policies that are concerned with aesthetics or neighborhood character (and may influence which aspects of the project need to be shown)?
- Are there other developments existing or planned in the area?
- Are there strong patterns of seasonal or daily atmospheric conditions, lighting, traffic, and the like that would affect views of the project?

If practical, a brief site reconnaissance is very helpful in focusing on important issues.

DETERMINE WHO WILL BE THE AUDIENCE OR INTERPRETERS OF THE SIMULATIONS

- the public
- the client or project sponsor
- the project design or engineering team
- regulatory or review agencies
- local landowners and special-interest groups
- potential investors
- environmental consultants conducting impact studies
- judge and jury

Also, try to determine what level of exposure to and understanding of simulations the audience has.

IDENTIFY GENERAL VIEWS TO BE SIMULATED. This is the stage at which the representativeness of the simulations is established. Ideally, this part of the process can be coordinated with or replaced by a visual analysis (see Chapter 3). If this is not possible

- Identify major viewing areas that would be representative of typical and important views experienced by the public and affected interest groups (such as different residential communities, parks, major or scenic highways, resorts, and public gathering places). Appendix A provides criteria for selecting such views. This can be done with maps and/or during a site reconnaissance trip. The latter may not pinpoint precise viewpoint locations; this is not necessary (and may even be a waste of time) if a second trip can be made once simulation planning is complete.
- Identify any important project characteristics to be shown (such as public transit facilities during rush hour, landscaping schemes after ten years of plant growth, or ski runs during summer and winter).

DETERMINE THE APPROXIMATE QUANTITY OF SIMULATION IMAGES REQUIRED. How many do you need to fulfill the purpose of the simulation exercise, while still meeting the fundamental objectives of comprehension, credibility, and lack of bias?

Select the Simulation Method

This task defines how the simulations will be produced and presented. This is the stage at which functional requirements, such as cost and schedule, enter the picture and need to be balanced against the specific purpose and fundamental objectives of the simulation.

This is also the stage at which the simulation medium is chosen. There are, however, other important decisions to be made first; in particular, the type of simulation and the appropriate level of abstraction needs to be determined and the final presentation medium (or media) identified. The original simulation medium needs to be compatible with both these choices.

DETERMINE THE TYPE OF SIMULATION. A general guide to the types of simulation that are appropriate to the different applications of simulation is given in Table 7-2. The decision on whether simulations are to be *generic* (based on project assumptions) or *specific* (based on an actual project design) is usually straightforward: if detailed project designs have been developed and show exact locations, dimensions, and materials, then specific simulations normally would be prepared; if no such designs are yet available, only generic simulations are possible. Either type of simulation can potentially be employed for most project applications (Table 7-2), but, clearly, where simulations are to be used for final design review, construction guides, or systematic postconstruction evaluation, specific simulations are required.

The other principal decision to make on the type of simulation is the appropriate level of abstraction. (This decision should be made before the choice of medium is finalized.) As has been described earlier, simulations can be *conceptual,* showing basic underlying relationships usually in an abstract or diagrammatic manner, or *experiential,* revealing more of the detail or precision that an observer might see or experience in a real environment.

There are two principal questions to answer in determining how abstract or precise the simulation should be:

1. *Should conceptual or severely abstract simulations be used at all?*

    The answer to this depends on the purpose of the simulation. Conceptual or abstract simulations can be useful on their own if the purpose of the simulation is to express quick design ideas between people with a similar level of understanding, or to explain a general relationship such as relative building heights (Fig. 7-2*a*). For most other project planning purposes, however, severely abstract simulations are not suitable unless accompanied by more experiential or precise simulations capable of expressing aesthetic design character or perceptual nuances. There is simply too much room for misinterpretation of abstract images as the only tool for visualizing future landscapes (see Chapter 6).

2. *How precise do the simulations have to be?*

    Once the need for less abstract simulations has been established, the question becomes one of the level of precision required. As described in Chapter 6, since we cannot yet reliably predict how each type of inaccuracy will affect bias, it is safest to aim for higher accuracy and precision. However, given the necessity for simple as well as sophisticated approaches to simulation, the user should choose between two basic approaches:

- Accepting a moderate level of abstraction where, for example, lack of project data or limited abilities of the preparer could otherwise lead to inaccurate portrayals or low credibility if precise simulation were attempted. *Moderate abstraction* is defined as having some image elements (such as color, texture, and details of edges and forms) in simplified form or

TABLE 7-2. TYPES OF SIMULATION APPROPRIATE TO DIFFERENT APPLICATIONS

Application of Simulation in Project Planning	Generic	Specific	
	Conceptual Simulations (Abstract)	Experiential Simulations (Precise or Moderately Abstract)	
Design/internal planning	X	X	—
General orientation	X*	X	X
Environmental assessment	X*	X	X
Mitigation planning	X*	X	X
Agency/legal decision-making	X*	X	X
Construction guides	—	—	X
Monitoring	—	—	X

*If presented in combination with more precise simulations where aesthetic judgments are required or interpreters include non-designers.

a

b

c

Figure 7-2. Different levels of abstraction in simulations of multistory buildings: example of a simulation with severe abstraction (a); example of a simulation with moderate abstraction (b); example of a simulation with high precision (simulated building indicated by arrow) (c).

even omitted (see Fig. 7-2b). Position, scale, overall shape, and tonal variations, however, should be shown.

- Aiming for precise simulations with high overall accuracy (Fig. 7-2c), minimizing the risk of bias caused by differences between the actual view and the simulation. Fully *precise simulations* show all or most image elements, including colors, textures, and details of the scene.

In both cases, the level of distortion should be low, that is, the position, scale, shape, and tones or colors shown should be generally correct, regardless of the level of detail. Figure 2-19 illustrates the range of abstraction (from severely abstract to precise), in alternative depictions of a single project.

The evidence reviewed in Chapter 6 suggests that both the moderately abstract and precise approaches, if properly carried out, have high credibility, are easily understood, and carry a lower risk of misleading users than do simulations with considerable abstraction (Fig. 7-2a) or distortion (see Fig. 6-22).

The question of when it is appropriate to use one or other of the two approaches depends upon a number of factors, as indicated in Figure 7-3 and Table 7-3. The predominant factor is the level of the preparer's expertise or experience available. Obtaining high accuracy in simulation usually requires personnel with considerable graphics training or skill in the use of sophisticated equipment. The approach of moderate abstraction, on the other hand, lies within the grasp of many less experienced people who routinely are involved in project planning and have some basic graphic skills.

Many situations occur where time and budget constraints preclude the use of sophisticated techniques or highly skilled preparers of simulations, yet some sort of graphic support for project review is required. If the budget is fixed, it may also be better to have several moderately abstract simulations rather than one or two precise simulations. The problem here is to hold down the cost and complexity of the simulation process without sacrificing the fairness and credibility of the simulations produced.

With more precise simulations, it is necessary and cost effective to use qualified and experienced illustrators, model-makers, or computer simulation specialists. By using experts, credibility problems due to obvious errors can be

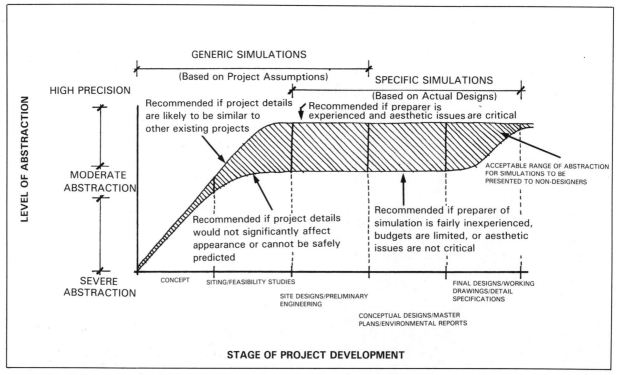

Figure 7-3. Relationship of abstraction to the level of project data available.

TABLE 7-3.   SELECTING THE APPROPRIATE SIMULATION APPROACH

| Selection Factors | Simulation Requirements | |
	High Accuracy Overall	Moderate Abstraction
Personnel	Highly trained, experienced, often specialized staff; for example, artists, computer-programmers, model-builders, and film makers. Often consultants conduct entire simulation work.	Staff requiring some knowledge of project issues, understanding of project plans, knowledge of elementary graphic techniques. Often in-house, though with consultants providing some assistance.
Equipment	Specialized equipment such as airbrushes, video cameras, solid-modeling computer graphics.	Basic photography equipment and graphics supplies.
Data available	Detailed project specifications, designs/photographs of similar projects, color samples, detailed landscape plans.	General project specifications and design data.
Cost	Relatively high labor rates and/or equipment/materials costs.	Labor and expenses are similar to other in-house work.
Project issues	Project is highly controversial; project has been or is likely to be criticized on aesthetic grounds or for specific visual features; project is designed in detail to address potential visual concerns.	Project aesthetics may be a concern but visual details are not crucial.
Audience/presentation format	Simulation(s) to be presented to a sophisticated group expecting considerable attention to detail; simulations to be part of a high-quality graphics package or media presentation.	Simulations to be reproduced simply in normal report format for in-house analysis, for general orientation, or to support general study findings.
Time available	May require time to obtain/organize preparers, or to carry out complicated simulations.	If routinely carried out, can be accomplished rapidly.

avoided, particularly where preparers of simulations are familiar with the type of project being shown, the site, the aesthetic issues surrounding the project, and the medium they are asked to use. However, there is a definite risk that using some outside experts without some sort of supervision or review can result in simulations that appear too slick, arousing distrust in users. Formulaic graphic tricks, uncorroborated guesswork, and highly developed individual styles should not be accepted. The sales-drawing approach of making projects appear more attractive than in reality, or of showing them only in their best light, may be ingrained in the work of many illustrators, but it is not appropriate for planning and public issues. The objective should be to attain a neutral, almost anonymous approach in which the character of the preparer does not intrude upon the context of the picture.

Either the moderately abstract or precise approach to simulation can be applied to both generic and specific types of simulation. The degree of abstraction that is appropriate for a generic simulation, however, may depend upon the level of project data available (see Fig. 7-3) and also on the type of project. If the project is typical of others that have been built, then photographs of similar projects may permit fairly detailed generic simulations even without much project data. If the project is complex or unprecedented, it could be misleading to assume project design details, and would be safer to use a moderately abstract image.

The sections (below) on preparing simulations are written separately for the two kinds of simulation preparers (experienced and relatively inexperienced) and the corresponding levels of abstraction (precise and moderately abstract).

It should be recognized that the spread of user-friendly, relatively sophisticated image-processing programs on personal computers is making it possible for relatively inexperienced people to prepare fairly precise simulations with some ease. This presents great opportunities and enormous dangers, since very distorted but convincing simulations may result where an incorrect simulation process has been followed. The steps recommended for more experienced preparers should be followed with these media.

SELECT THE APPROPRIATE MEDIUM FOR CREATING SIMULATIONS. It is tempting to provide a completed matrix of the advantages and disadvantages of various media measured against criteria of simulation quality, as proposed by Appleyard.[1] However, as pointed out on numerous occasions in this book, there are so many other variables that can be more important in determining simulation quality that such a matrix would be almost meaningless as a guide to selecting appropriate media. There are, however, some generalities and inherent qualities of media that typically hold true; so, with some reservations, the author has provided a matrix that highlights some important aspects of the various media available (Table 7-4).

TABLE 7-4. SOME GENERAL ADVANTAGES AND DISADVANTAGES OF SIMULATION MEDIA

Media	Principles								Functional Considerations					
	Fundamentals			Representativeness	Accuracy	Visual Clarity	Interest	Legitimacy	Cost	Flexibility	Ease	Speed	Portability	Durability
	Understanding	Credibility	Bias											
Rendering				D. May omit project context	D. Least constraints on inaccuracy				Unit costs: low to high; Equipment costs: low	Fair	Easy to difficult	Fast to slow	Good	May degenerate with time
■ Line	G	P	P											
■ Tonal	G	P	P											
■ Full Color	G	P	P											
Photomontage				A. Possible to show alternative viewing conditions (e.g., lighting); A. Shows project context				A. Relationship to reality is clear	Unit costs: low; Equipment costs: low	Fair	Easy to difficult	Fast	Good	Degenerates with time
■ Black & White	Varies	P	P											
■ Full Color	Varies	Varies	Varies											
Photo Retouching				A. Possible to show alternative viewing conditions; A. Shows project context	A. Photograph imposes constraints on inaccuracy			A. Relationship to reality is clear	Unit costs: moderate; Equipment costs: low	Fair	Difficult	Varies	Good	Degenerates with time
■ Black & White	G	Varies	P											
■ Full Color	G	G	G											
Multiple Projection	Varies	P	?	A. As for photomontage		D. Often poor	A. Limited special effects		Unit costs: low; Equipment costs: moderate	Low	Easy	Fast	Poor	Degenerates with time
Computer Perspective				A. Multiple views easily produced	A. Eliminates guesswork on scale, position, and shape	A/D. Varies	A. Good if interactive	A. Visible documentation of data	Unit costs: low to high; Equipment costs: moderate to high	High	Moderate to difficult	Fast	Good	Easily stored and regenerated
■ Wire-Frame	Varies	G	P											
■ Hand-Rendered	Varies	G	?											
■ Solid-Modeled	G	?	?											
■ Texture-Mapped	?	?	?											
Videosimulation				A. As for photomontage; A. Multiple views easily produced		D. Resolution limits	A. Special effects		Unit costs: low; Equipment costs: moderate to high	High	Easy to moderate	Fast	Fair	Easily stored and regenerated
■ Low Resolution	G	Varies	?											
■ High Resolution	G	G	?											
Animated Computer Graphics				A. Multiple and sequential views possible	A. Eliminates guesswork on scale, position, and shape		A. Motion involves the viewer		Unit costs: high to very high; Equipment costs: high to very high	Fair	Difficult	Varies	Fair	
■ Wire-Frame	Varies	?	?											
■ Solid-Modeled	G	G	?											
■ Texture-Mapped	?	?	?											

Media	Fundamentals			Principles					Functional Considerations					
	Under-standing	Credibility	Bias	Representativeness	Accuracy	Visual Clarity	Interest	Legitimacy	Cost	Flexibility	Ease	Speed	Portability	Durability
Film/Video Matting	?	?	?	A. Multiple and se-quential views possible			A. Motion in-volves the viewer	Low	*Unit costs:* high *Equipment costs:* high to very high	Fair	Difficult	Slow		
Hologram	?	?	?	A. Multiple views possible			A. Novelty		*Unit costs:* very high *Equipment costs:* very high	Low	Difficult		Poor	
Model ▪ Simple ▪ Detailed	Varies G	Varies G	P G	A. Multiple views possible D. Often omits project context	A. Eliminates guess-work on scale, po-sition, and shape			A. Visible documen-tation of data	*Unit costs:* moder-ate to high *Equipment costs:* low to moder-ate	Low	Easy to dif-ficult	Fast to slow	Poor	Difficult to store
Site Mock-up ▪ Scale Markers ▪ Project Replica	G G	G G	? ?	A. Multiple views possible A. Shows project context	A. As for models			A. Relation-ship to reality is clear	*Unit costs:* moder-ate *Equipment costs:* moder-ate		Easy	Fast		

Key
G. Typically good
P. Potential problems

A. Advantage
D. Disadvantage

An appropriate medium is one that fits the desired simulation approach and available resources of those preparing the simulation images. This choice depends on the level of abstraction required.

For *moderately abstract simulations* and *less experienced preparers,* suggested media include

Simple drawings showing major tonal or full-color patterns of project and context (see Fig. 7-2*b*).

Photomontage with tonal or full-color patterns, created by overlaying onto a print of the existing scene a simple drawing of the project (see Fig. 2-19*c*) or a photograph of a three-dimensional study model in the same view. This can save considerable time in comparison with a rendering of the full scene.

Computer-generated line drawing or wireframe image with hidden-line removal (obtained from a consultant if necessary), to which tonal or full-color patterns are added by hand (for example, with pen markers as in Plate 25), or by simple shading or solid-modeling programs. The computer graphics help substantiate the accuracy of the final product but may not be cost effective if only one or two views per site are required.

Study models (Fig. 7-4) with tree symbols, sheets of cardboard, or other material representing topographic contours, and design elevations or photographs of building facades pasted onto model buildings; all of which can be viewed through a hand-held modelscope to provide ground-level views. This medium allows less flexibility in changing colors and details, and makes it hard to include sufficient site context in typical views.

For *precise simulations* and *more experienced preparers,* suggested media are those that are capable of producing detailed and fairly realistic images, preferably in full color. These include

Figure 7-4. Study model of a commercial development.

Precise rendering or illustrative drawing and painting, using traditional illustration tools but in a fairly restrained, neutral, and realistic manner based on site photography (Fig. 7-5 and Plate 26). This can require considerable time and skill to build up a realistic picture of a single project view.

Detailed and colored *three-dimensional models* seen through a periscope or model-scope to give ground views, which can be very convincing and permit movement in any direction (see Fig. 4-3). Such models are, however, expensive to build at a scale large enough to provide realistic images that include background and surrounding landscapes.

High-resolution color *computer graphics.* These techniques are developing quickly with advances such as ray-tracing, fractal imagery, and anti-aliasing, but realistic images totally synthesized by computer remain extremely expensive. This is especially true for non-architectural objects where detailed and highly variable landscape surfaces or intricate objects are to be simulated (Plate 27).[2] Solid-modeling packages becoming more available at the personal computer level are not yet able to produce images of this precision. However, the combination of solid-modeling with video-capture of real-world surface textures (known as *texture mapping*) may soon make more realistic simulations of natural landscapes possible.

Film and video manipulations (such as blue-matte superimposition and video image processing). These media range from highly sophisticated movie techniques to relatively affordable and user-friendly video simulation programs (see Fig. 1-4 and Plate 24). The latter can be used to digitize instantly either photographic slides or video frames, and alter or superimpose objects on the computer screen by way of an electronic drawing tablet (Fig. 7-6). It is a relatively cheap medium, but is currently limited in the resolution of hard-copy output generally available.[3] Before long, however, this technique, combined with high-resolution computer imagery and hard-copy output, will begin to replace manual techniques (see below) in all applications.

Figure 7-5.   Precise rendering of transit facility.

Figure 7-6. Drawing tablet and computer equipment for video image processing.

Meanwhile, it provides a very effective and cost-efficient way to produce multiple simulations of generic project alternatives, at a fairly high level of precision, for rapid group decision-making based on video presentations.

Photosimulation, using high-quality photography. This medium can provide a highly accurate and totally convincing image in which the preparer is almost forced to match the level of color, detail, lighting, and other qualities of the actual scene. This can be done in several ways: by superimposing a precise rendering of the project onto the photograph of the site (Fig. 7-7); by superimposing one piece of a photograph onto another photograph (Fig. 7-8); by superimposing a photograph of a precise model (where one exists) onto the base photograph (Fig. 7-9); by retouching a photograph directly using paints or dyes (Fig. 7-10 and Plate 28); or by a combination of these techniques (Plate 29). In most cases, photosimulation requires less time than a precise rendering does, since there is no need to simulate the project surroundings, and effort can be focused solely upon the part of the scene that would be altered by the project. This medium is also the easiest to relate to existing conditions in photographs and to built projects in postconstruction appraisal. It usually takes considerably longer than lower-resolution video image processing, however.

If in doubt about which simulation medium to use, there may be opportunities to use more than one in combination, to offset any disadvantages or limitations of using a single medium. This can

Figure 7-7. Photomontage using a rendering of condominiums.

a

b

Figure 7-8. Photomontage using photographs of waterfront landscape elements.

Figure 7-9. Photomontage using a photograph of a model of an office building (shown by an arrow).

Plate 1. Videosimulation of an existing building superimposed on a different site.

2a

2b

2c

Plate 2. Renderings of Antony House by Humphry Repton: existing conditions (with flap in place) *(a);* flap used to show the existing conditions to be altered *(b);* proposed design, revealed by folding back the flap *(c).*

Plate 3. Simulation required for a proposed wind-turbine development in San Gorgonio Pass, Riverside County, California.

4a

4b

4c

Plate 4. Computer graphics which model the expected growth of landscaping established to mitigate powerline impacts.

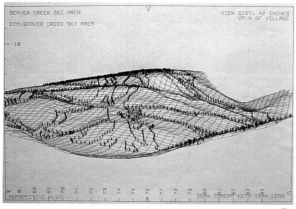

5a

5b

5c

5d

Plate 5. Time-lapse photography used to monitor progress of ski run development at Beaver Creek, Colorado: perspective plot simulation of proposed ski runs *(a);* same view before development (August 1975) *(b);* view after development (September 1979) *(c);* view after further development (February 1981) *(d).*

6a

6b

Plate 6. Vegetative management alternatives for the Blue Ridge Parkway, North Carolina: photosimulation of views with mowing and cutting *(a)*; photograph showing effects of natural growth on scenic views *(b)*.

7a

7b

Plate 7. Photograph of existing conditions *(a)* along Interstate 25 in Denver, Colorado, and a photosimulation *(b)* of proposed busways.

8a

8b

Plate 8. Scenic quality: relatively high where diverse landscape elements fit together harmoniously in a distinctive landscape *(a)*; relatively low where landscape is monotonous and undistinctive *(b)*.

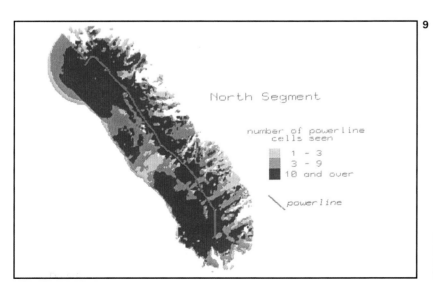

9

North Segment

number of powerline
cells seen

1 - 3
3 - 9
10 and over

powerline

Plate 9. Viewshed map, showing the area of land from which a powerline would be visible, with different viewing frequencies.

10a

10b

Plate 10. Views of the same object seen in different directions with different lighting conditions: frontlighting (viewing the illuminated side) *(a)*; backlighting (viewing the shaded side) *(b)*.

11

Plate 11. Factors affecting visual prominence of a project color: The predominant colors in this scene are the medium-value blues of sea and sky, with beige and low-chroma greens in the backdrop. The chromatic yellow and reflective white of the offshore facility contrast strongly with its background.

12a

12b

Plate 12. View of a model *(b)* which, when shown in a movie sequence to study participants at U.C. Berkeley, was mistaken for film footage of a real drive through the landscape *(a)*.

Plate 13. Photo-retouched simulation of Liquid National Gas terminal (center of picture) in the Santa Barbara channel, California, at sunset.

Plate 14. Comparison of two photosimulations showing distant proposed power line in the Gore Pass area of Colorado: during daylight *(a)*; at dusk *(b)*, shown in response to public concerns for impacts on sunset views. From *Foundations for Visual Project Review,* R. C. Smardon, J. Palmer, and J. Felleman (eds.) © 1986 John Wiley & Sons.

14a

14b

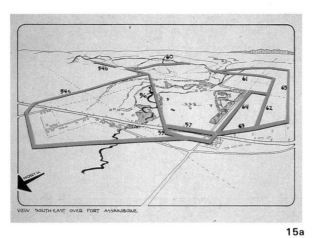

15a

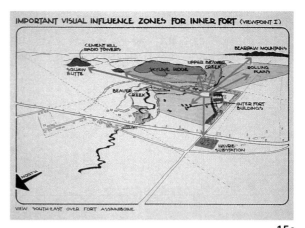

IMPORTANT VISUAL INFLUENCE ZONES FOR INNER FORT (VIEWPOINT I)

CEMENT HILL RADIO TOWERS

BEARPAW MOUNTAINS

SQUAW BUTTE

SKYLINE RIDGE

UPPER BEAVER CREEK

ROLLING PLAINS

BEAVER CREEK

OUTER FORT BUILDINGS

HAVRE SUBSTATION

NORTH

VIEW SOUTH-EAST OVER FORT ASSINNIBOINE

15e

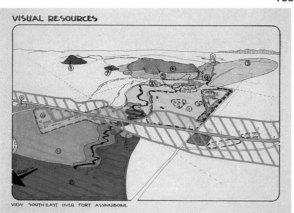

VISUAL RESOURCES

NORTH

VIEW SOUTH-EAST OVER FORT ASSINNIBOINE

15b

15f

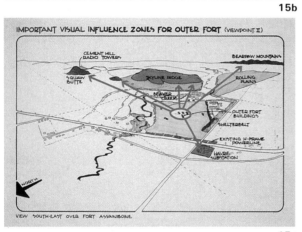

IMPORTANT VISUAL INFLUENCE ZONES FOR OUTER FORT (VIEWPOINT II)

CEMENT HILL RADIO TOWERS

BEARPAW MOUNTAINS

SQUAW BUTTE

SKYLINE RIDGE

ROLLING PLAINS

BEAVER CREEK

OUTER FORT BUILDINGS

SHELTERBELT

EXISTING H-FRAME POWERLINE

HAVRE SUBSTATION

NORTH

VIEW SOUTH-EAST OVER FORT ASSINNIBOINE

15c

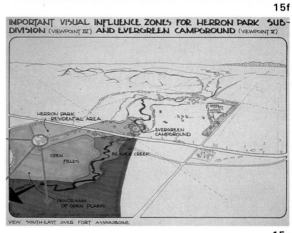

IMPORTANT VISUAL INFLUENCE ZONES FOR HERRON PARK SUB-DIVISION (VIEWPOINT IV) AND EVERGREEN CAMPGROUND (VIEWPOINT V)

HERRON PARK RESIDENTIAL AREA

EVERGREEN CAMPGROUND

OPEN FIELDS

BEAVER CREEK

NORTH

PANORAMA OF OPEN PLAINS

VIEW SOUTH-EAST OVER FORT ASSINNIBOINE

15g

15d

15h

Plate 15. Important viewpoints representing views of proposed alternative routes for a power line near the historic site of Fort Assinniboine, Montana: aerial view showing alternative power line links *(a)*; important visual influence zones surrounding the fort *(b)*; important views from outer fort *(c)*; photosimulation of Link 56 from outer fort *(d)*; important views from inner fort *(e)*; photosimulation of Link 63 from inner fort *(f)*; important views from nearby residential areas *(g)*; photosimulation of Link 54c from residential area *(h)*.

Plate 16. Photograph of actual view of the same project

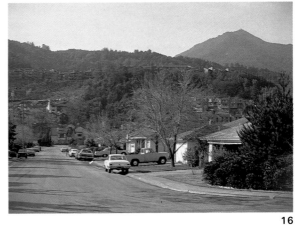

16

17a

17b

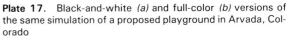

Plate 17. Black-and-white *(a)* and full-color *(b)* versions of the same simulation of a proposed playground in Arvada, Colorado

Plate 18. Residential project, Marin County, California: black-and-white photomontage of project *(a)*; photograph of actual view *(b)*.

18a

18b

19a

19b

21a

21b

20

Plate 19. Bridge, near Walnut Creek, California: model of white bridge *(a)*; photograph of actual bridge with less contrasting treatment *(b)* (*Source:* S. Sheppard 1982).

Plate 20. Rendering in a style typically used in sales drawings, containing several elements that emphasize activity, drama, and excitement.

Plate 21. Geothermal power plant, Geysers, California: full-color simulation (*a*); photograph of actual project (*b*), showing different colors and color contrasts which cannot be attributed solely to different lighting conditions or color reproduction.

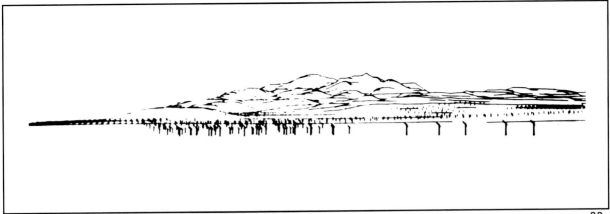

22a

22b

Plate 22. Simulation of wind turbines with a computer-graphic software program (*a*), able to show only lines (© Dynamic Graphics, Inc); simulation of wind turbines by photo retouching (*b*), a medium capable of showing all image elements except motion.

23a

23b

23c

Plate 23. Different reproductions of a photosimulation of proposed telecommunication facilities: original color simulation (*a*); screened black-and-white version (*b*); photocopy of original (*c*).

24a

24c

24b

24d

Plate 24. Hard-copy reproductions of a video image, showing housing with and without street-trees; using a dot-matrix printer (a,b); using computer-generated color separations (c,d).

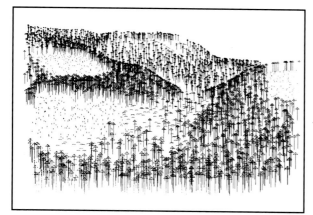

25a

SP=(60.   .-25.) CP=(75..40.) SP-ELEV=4000. AOP=40.YEAR= 0.
1 HOUR ~ BLACK FELT TIPS (══)
            ⅄ WHITE PRISMACOLOR

25b

SP=(60.   .-25.) CP=(75..40.) SP-ELEV=4000. AOP=40.YEAR= 1.
1 HOUR TO RENDER — MAGIC MARKER ON REVERSE.

25c

Plate 25. Computer graphic with additional rendering by hand: original computer graphic (*a*); black and white (*b*); color (*c*).

Plate 26. Precise rendering of transit facility.

27

Plate 27. Computer-generated full-color image showing an unusual amount of detail.

28a

28b

Plate 28. Photo retouching by "painting in" a substation, fence, and overhead wires (b) onto a base photograph (a).

29a

29b

Plate 29. Simulation (b) of proposed expressway, produced by a combination of montage and retouching on the base photograph (a).

30a

30b

Plate 30. Example of Austrop-MacNeil Powerline simulations in full color: before (*a*) and after (*b*) of powerline Link 5 seen through the window of Christ Sanctuary, Brentwood Church.

31a

31b

Plate 31. Black-and-white photosimulation of the proposed Bottle Rock Geothermal Power Plant from a viewpoint on the opposite hillside (*a*); Photograph of actual project, taken from a viewpoint close to that in Plate 31a (*b*).

a

b

Figure 7-10. Photo retouching by "painting in" a substation, fence, and overhead wires (*b*) onto a base photograph (*a*).

be done easily, for example, where a precise scale model has already been built and can be inserted by montage into photosimulations or videosimulations, for relatively little extra expense.

Choice of media is likely to change quickly in the coming years as computer technology advances and prices continue to drop. There is likely to be an increasing shift away from renderings, models, and photomontage in favor of computer and video techniques. The realism and resolution of photosimulation and of the most elaborate computer imagery will set the standards that lower-end computer technologies will strive to achieve. The demand for realism will probably continue the predominance of photo-based and video-based images. At the same time, more interactive techniques and cheaper animation will become available.

DETERMINE THE SIMULATION BUDGET. The ap-propriate budget for simulation can be gauged either by the value of its contribution to the project planning process, or by the cost of producing the simulations. There can be enormous disparities between the two measures. Simulations costing a couple of thousand dollars can save millions of dollars further down the road if they help to avoid poor decisions. Nevertheless, in the public sector, especially, it is often difficult to quantify the worth of a simulation, and in the private sector there are often extreme pressures to minimize costs that could reduce profits. Consequently, the cost of preparing simulations is most often the basis for budgeting. Table 7-4 compares some very general costs of different media, and Appendix B presents some indication of how unit costs vary with three increasingly common simulation media: wire-frame computer graphics on a personal computer, photosimulations, and videosimulation (video image processing).

SELECT THE PREPARER(S) OF THE SIMULATION. Once a simulation approach has been selected, identify potential preparers. Simulations should only be prepared in-house if there are suitably trained or capable staff with the correct equipment. Most projects are too important to be used as a learning exercise for draftsmen or would-be artists, unless simulations are carried out under the supervision of a trained preparer. At the same time, there are on the staff of many firms and government agencies personnel capable of producing adequate simulations using the moderate abstraction approach, if they follow the process explained in this chapter.

More precise simulations require skilled preparers, most of whom operate as freelance consultants, specialized firms, or specialized groups within multidisciplinary firms. There are no universal standards, qualifications, or associations for such professionals (other than architectural illustrators), which often makes it hard to locate appropriate individuals. Reputation works best, but check references and talk to past clients or reviewing agencies to ensure that contracts have been honored and that simulations have been of high quality; and confirm that the same key individuals who delivered good simulations last time will be available to work on the current project. When interviewing prospective consultants, ask to see examples of simulations and corresponding photographs of projects as built. There are many good artists who do not know how to produce an accurate simulation. Do not select solely on the basis of low bid—you may get what you pay for. Be wary of simulation consultants who resist your attempts to coordinate closely with them, review their work in progress, or discuss their approach. However, do not select a yes-man. Consultants of this sort will show only what they think their client wants to see and will not apprise you of possible design or simulation problems that could cause grief at a later stage. Look for consultants who are likely to be around for some time and will be well prepared to defend their work if the project becomes embroiled in controversy. On projects with any sort of public or regulatory issue, avoid simulation preparers who have a strong reputation for preparing sales drawings.

DETERMINE THE SCHEDULE FOR SIMULATION. Most simulations can be produced fairly quickly (in a matter of a few weeks or less) unless

- available expertise and/or equipment is tied up
- there is a need to wait for a different season or other environmental condition in which to photograph or record site views
- an extensive series of complex images, or a large detailed model, needs to be prepared
- there is a delay in obtaining project information that is necessary in order to prepare the simulation accurately

Do not postpone simulation planning to the last minute—the quality of simulation will suffer if time constraints become too severe. Allow enough time for contingencies such as the need for a return visit to the site if the weather is bad the first time, or delays in finding or developing important project description data.

Most simulation techniques can be speeded up to some extent, although the costs incurred may rise substantially, as with rush charges on photographic and reproduction services. Certain media permit very rapid generation of images, even to the point of making possible the concept of interactive workshops with production of simulations on demand. Chief among these are sketching by hand and video image processing, which allows electronic montage of elements captured on the screen. In general, however, the more sophisticated the medium and the more precise the simulation, the longer the simulation will take.

DETERMINE THE MEDIUM AND FORMAT FOR PRESENTATION (see also GUIDELINES FOR PRESENTING SIMULATIONS). Although a given simulation image may be presented in several different ways (as described in Chapter 5), the choice of original simulation medium may preclude the use of a particular reproduction technique, and vice versa. Table 7-5 provides recommendations on selecting appropriate presentation media for a given original simulation medium. Possible choices of medium for reproduction, dissemination, and presentation of simulations include the following:

- *Reports.* Ubiquitously used in environmental assessments, they require high-quality images for mass reproduction. Since the cost of printing full-color separations is expensive, reproduced simulations usually are seen only in black and white. There may therefore be no point in preparing simulations in full color originally if key decision-makers will see only reports in black and white.

  Offset printing with half-tones can convey the precision of tonal simulations quite well. Normal photo-copying of simulation material is to be discouraged generally since visual clarity and consistency suffer greatly. Line drawings and wire-frame computer output are the principal types of simulation that can withstand such treatment without significant degradation. Black-and-white and color laser-prints are making it simpler to produce better copies cheaply. Currently, videosimulations and computer animations do not lend themselves well to the static hard-copy presentation media readily available, although the technology is advancing rapidly with development of higher-resolution photographic prints from digital computer images.

- *Mounted boards and projected color slides.* These permit large, full-color simulations to be seen at better viewing angles than smaller images in reports, and allow many people to see a limited number of images at public meetings and displays. Both slides and boards can be transported readily, although slides require basic projection equipment and control of room lighting. Boards can be taken to the site for purposes of postconstruction monitoring.

- *Backlit transparency with a viewing device or booth.* This correctly positions the viewer at the appropriate distance from the image (which can be important where the apparent scale of the project is an issue). It also controls lighting and can provide wraparound wide-angle views of panoramic scenes (see Fig. 7-16). The cost of construction and relocation of the booth, however, may be significant, and viewing by numbers of people one at a time takes longer than with wall-mounted exhibits. This technique is appropriate for more sophisticated photosimulations on highly sensitive projects.

- *Computer monitor, video screen, or film screen.* These are the best presentation systems for animation, live footage, or low-resolution computer graphics. Video can also be used to given an idea of how a project would look in moving views by inserting static simulations into a travel sequence at regular intervals. Most television screens and monitors have limited resolution to which people are accustomed, but many have a wide range of colors. Many other forms of simulation can be captured on video or film, including both static and dynamic original media (such as moving views of a model through a periscope or modelscope). Single small screens are useful only for small groups of individuals, while large video projection screens have historically been of poor visual clarity. All video screens limit the capability of viewing panoramic scenes, while film can provide a higher quality and wider angle image (even including wraparound images) if appropriate combinations of cameras are available.

- *Models.* Original models can be presented in the flesh, so to speak, which allows people to gain an overview of the whole project. Use of a modelscope is recommended to allow viewers to see eye-level scenes and select their own viewpoints.

- *Site presentations.* These are useful when on-site markers or full-scale project replicas have been erected, or when hard-copy simulations can be taken into the field.

Whichever presentation medium is chosen, establish specifications for reproduction techniques that will preserve the visual clarity of the simulations. For example, specifications can be developed for minimum line width on ink drawings that are to be reduced, the minimum resolution of video images to be output on hard copy, the number of colors necessary to distinguish important features on computer graphics, or the

TABLE 7-5. RECOMMENDED PRESENTATION MEDIA FOR ORIGINAL SIMULATION IMAGES

Original Simulation Image	Xerox Page	Printed Page	
		B&W	**Color**
Rendering			
— line	*	*	
— tone	+	*	
— full color		+	*
Photomontage			
— black & white	+	*	
— full color		+	*
Photo retouching			
— black & white	+	*	
— full color		+	*
Multiple projection		+	+
Static computer perspective			
— wire-frame	*	*	
— hand-rendered	+	+	+
— solid-modeling		+	+
— texture-mapping		+	*
Videosimulation			
— low resolution			+
— high resolution		+	*
Animated computer perspective			
—wire-frame		+	
—solid-modeling			+
—texture-mapping			+
Film/video animation by matting			+
Hologram			
Model			
— simple		+	
— detailed		+	+
Full-scale site mock-up			
— scale markers		+	+
— project replica		+	*

Key to overall ratings of presentation format:
* Good visual clarity, appropriate cost and technical requirements given the original medium.
+ Fair visual clarity, acceptable cost and technical requirements.

Mounted Board or Print (with or without Overlays)	Presentation Media							
	Color Slide	Backlit Transparency	Computer Monitor or Video Screen	Film Projection (16 mm)	Model	Model with Modelscope	Site Visit	Hologram
*								
*								
*	*		+					
*	+	+						
*	*	*	+					
*	+	+						
*	*	*	+					
	*	+						
*	+		*					
*	+		+					
+	+		*					
*	*	+	*					
	+		*					
*	*	*	+					
			*					
+	+		*					
+	+		*					
	+		*	*				
								*
+	+		+	+	+	*		
+	+		*	*	+	*		
+	*		*	*			*	
+	*		*	*			*	

125

minimum and maximum sizes at which images should be presented.

At the conclusion of this stage, there should be a plan or road map for the simulation process that identifies the approach, content, specific techniques, preparer, budget, schedule, audiences, and presentation format for simulation.

GUIDELINES FOR PREPARING SIMULATIONS

Collect Detailed Data

- Obtain all available and up-to-date plans, elevations, and descriptions of the proposed project and associated development and infrastructure. If possible, obtain photographs of similar projects that have been built. Talk to the project engineer or designer to resolve any questions and ensure adequate understanding of the project. Project data may include

  site plan (building locations, floor plans, roof plans, road layouts)
  building elevations and sections
  grading plan
  landscape plan and vegetation clearing plan
  design details and specifications

- Obtain topographic maps and, preferably, recent aerial photographs of the site and its surroundings. Appropriate scales may vary from

1 inch to 40 feet for detailed close-up simulations of small projects, to 1 inch to 2,000 feet (1 : 24,000) for distant views of large-scale projects. If computer perspectives are to be developed, the contour interval will be important for digitizing terrain data. Alternatively, digital elevation tapes can be ordered, if available at the appropriate resolution for the project site (for example, DEM and DMA data from US Geological Survey).

- Obtain information on any other developments planned in the vicinity.
- Consider viewing conditions of lighting, weather, and season, and select representative conditions to be portrayed from particular viewpoints (see Appendix A).
- Visit the site in those or similar conditions, and refine viewpoint locations (see Appendix A). Map and label final viewpoint locations precisely. If possible, mark the viewpoint position on the ground with an unobtrusive but permanent locatable sign such as a rock, stake, or spray-paint mark, or measure off its location from other permanent site features. Photograph in color the existing views, including any important travel sequences in which these viewpoints fall, and panoramas that show the landscape on both sides of the project site. Preferably include scale marker(s) on-site, for example, a car, person, survey rod, or site features of known height (Fig. 7-11). Document photographs taken, scale-marker dimensions and precise locations, and viewing conditions (see Field Recording Form in Appendix A). Measure or estimate the height of any structures or

Figure 7-11. Use of survey rod with flag to provide scale markers.

vegetation that might screen the project. As an alternative or supplement to photography, take color video footage of views and travel sequences.

Prepare Original Simulation Images

This section provides a general description of important considerations or tasks often left out of conventional graphics texts. For more detail on techniques, including simple perspective calculations to match simulations with photographs, consult Appendix A or texts listed in the Bibliography.

GENERAL GUIDELINES

- Create the original simulation(s) at an image size large enough to allow accurate delineation and image clarity when reproduced or projected. It is generally better to reduce a large image than to enlarge a small one (unless resolution can be improved simultaneously).
- Create simulations with a field-of-view wide enough to show the full site context, and, as a rule of thumb, not less than the angle of view in a standard 55 mm camera lens (about 40–45 degrees). Center the field-of-view in the direction of a typical real view, not necessarily on the project itself, since this may focus attention on it artificially. Conversely, do not choose a field-of-view that incorrectly places the project in an apparently peripheral position (Fig. 7-12).
- Use photographs of the existing site and similar completed projects as references during creation of the simulation(s). If using full color, try to obtain color specifications or samples for the project materials and disturbed site areas. Take into account the viewing conditions in order to estimate color contrasts as perceived from the viewpoint (colors generally become bluer, less brilliant, and less contrasty with distance).

GUIDELINES FOR LESS EXPERIENCED PREPARERS.
The following guidelines are offered for those without advanced skills in perspective construction, illustrative rendering, or sophisticated computer graphics.

- Create moderately abstract simulations without attempting precise rendering, so as to avoid criticism from users and inadvertent distortion of project appearance. For example, show major building masses, roof lines, eaves, floor levels or main windows, major landscaping, and major grading (see Fig. 7-2b); textures, architectural details, and smaller forms can be omitted.
- Use a "before" photograph either as a base for photomontage, or as an underlay or template for tracing the site context and scale markers.
- Avoid mistakes in structural elements (position, scale, and general form) by use of simple scaling techniques, such as photographing scale markers of known height on-site, generating computer-graphic perspectives, or making quick study models of project and site. Pay particular attention to scale, which is the hardest of the elements to estimate reliably by eye. Try to verify scale accuracy of computer graphics by comparing them with scale markers in site photographs, to double-check for major errors. Make sure that vanishing lines (straight lines seen in perspective) that

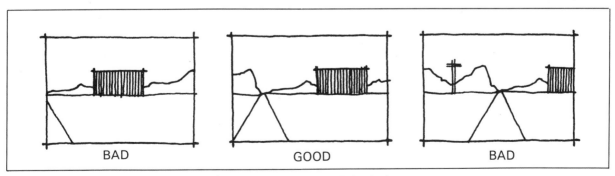

BAD   GOOD   BAD

Figure 7-12. Good and bad ways to center the field-of-view of a simulation in views from a road.

mark the edges or corners of proposed structures broadly match those of existing structures arranged on the same grid (see Appendix A for more details).

- Estimate expected tonal (light/dark) pattern (see Appendix A) and indicate by shading or Zipatone press-on film, so as to give scale and three-dimensional modeling to masses that otherwise would appear incorrectly to be uniform.

- Document your methods, calculations, and assumptions in producing the simulations.

GUIDELINES FOR MORE EXPERIENCED PREPARERS. The following guidelines are offered for skilled preparers familiar with perspective simulation techniques, or for those obtaining the services of such people.

- Create simulations that are accurate and reasonably precise or realistic, in full color if possible.

- Recognize that the intention is to show the project as it would be seen, and not necessarily to explain the project design.

- Work closely with project designers and/or regulatory staff who are familiar with the project and with similar projects and their effects on the landscape, so that subtle or complex relationships are not misrepresented.

- Visit the project site in order to understand it better.

- Do not use unrepresentative viewpoints specifically chosen to dramatize, downplay, or show off the project.

- Make sure that you are provided with full and exact project information and that objects are not selectively included or omitted from the simulation.

- Restrain artistic style and expression, and avoid sales gimmicks.

- Use the eye level, vanishing points, prevailing colors, and level of detail visible in the "before" photograph or video footage as a guide for the simulation work.

- Verify or cross-check automated (computer-generated) images for accuracy in scale or lighting (where shaded surfaces are depicted).

Review Simulations

If possible, have preliminary simulations reviewed by the project engineer or project designer before final simulations are completed, so that project designs can be altered if necessary and simulations corrected before further time and effort are wasted. Often, the preparer tends to be so close to the simulation that he or she may not see things that other people notice.

Before simulations are presented, have them reviewed again or appraised by a colleague or other appropriate person (other than the preparer) in order to identify any possible problems. This is discussed below, under Guidelines for Appraising Simulations, Preconstruction.

GUIDELINES FOR PRESENTING SIMULATIONS

- Reproduce simulations according to specifications laid down at the simulation planning stage; for example, do not magnify or reduce the image to the extent that visual clarity is impaired, or duplicate in such a way that tonal contrasts are lost. Revise these specifications if necessary to fit unforeseen aspects of the simulation. Since tonal qualities are of considerable importance in understanding and judging project designs, do not rely on photocopying to reproduce simulations, unless it has been determined that black-and-white line drawings are appropriate. Wherever originals contain color or tonal variations, use a halftone method of reproduction to convert the image to a fine dot pattern that can more clearly be reproduced (see Plate 23).

- Present simulations alongside the corresponding "before" photographs, in order to indicate views of existing features (attractive or unattractive) that would be lost, changed, obscured, or revealed. If using video, simulated images can be inserted or dissolved into footage of the existing view to provide the same sort of comparison.

- Present simulations at a large size, at a viewing angle close to the original field-of-view of the scene as illustrated in Figure 6-10, in order to approximate the real impact the project would have from the given viewpoint. For an image of a given size, this viewing angle dictates the correct distance from which the image should be viewed. Table 7-6 provides appropriate viewing distances for images of different sizes, assuming an angle of view approximating that of a typical camera lens. Appendix A provides a simple method for calculating this viewing distance. The ratio of width to height in the image should be similar to the oblong field of vision actually obtained by the eyes; 35 mm cameras more closely approximate this ratio than many larger-format cameras (for example, view cameras with 2 1/2 × 2 1/2-inch negatives) and video recorders. Simulations should not normally be extensively cropped at the sides for the same reason, but simulations based on squarer photographic formats should be cropped at top and bottom (Fig. 7-13). One of the disadvantages of video is that the television image is almost square and cannot replicate the actual field of vision without the use of distracting upper and lower borders.

The field-of-view shown in the simulation should be indicated to the user if it diverges significantly from the normal lens (for example, "This picture is equivalent to a telephoto shot"). It is important to indicate the correct viewing distance between the image and the user's eye. Various ways to permit users to obtain the correct viewing angle are possible, as follows:

Long, foldout panoramas can be inserted in reports (Fig. 7-14).

If budget limitations preclude the use of large illustrations in reports, a combination could be used of a wide-angle view to show the simulated project in its context, with a narrower-angle close-up of the simulated project to provide a view that is more conveniently seen at the correct viewing distance (Fig. 7-15).

Where slide or video presentations are used, seating for small groups can be arranged to control the image-to-user distance. Video projection screens can be used to increase the number of people able to see the simulation at the correct viewing angle.

A simulation booth, or kiosk with a curved image around the user (Fig. 7-16) can present a 180-degree (or even 360-degree) field-of-view to the user at the correct viewing distance.

- Provide map with viewpoints keyed to simulations (Fig. 7-17) and a rationale for selection of those viewpoints.
- Provide a description of the project design data used, assumptions made in portraying the project, unavoidable omissions of objects due to lack of data, any other inevitable inaccuracies, and viewing conditions in which project appearance would differ from that shown.
- Summarize or present evidence showing how the simulations were prepared and how accuracy has been assured. Where possible, give the accuracy level or margin of error expected.
- Allow for direct, side-by-side comparison of simulations showing different views, alternative project designs, or different viewing conditions.
- Design and review simulation titles, labels, and accompanying information carefully to avoid obscuring the simulation, distracting attention from it, or biasing people's responses to it. Labels and symbols to identify project or landscape features in the simulation can be shown on a lift-up overlay that allows the unaltered simulation to be viewed on its own.
- Plan and conduct the presentation sequence to maintain the viewers' interest and avoid

TABLE 7-6.   RELATIONSHIP OF VIEWING DISTANCE TO SIMULATION IMAGE SIZE FOR A 45-DEGREE VIEWING ANGLE

Image Size (width)	Ideal Viewing Distance (approximate)
5 in. (width of 3 × 5 in. print)	6 in.
8 in. (width of normal page in vertical report format)	9–10 in.
11 in. (width of normal page in horizontal report format)	13 in. (typical reading distance)
14 in. (width of 8 1/2 × 14 in. page or 11 × 14 in. print)	17 in.
17 in. (width of page in 11 × 17 in. foldout)	20–21 in.
20 in. (width of 16 × 20 in. print)	24 in.
36 in. (width of 24 × 36 in. print)	43–44 in.
5 ft. (width of typical projection screen)	6 ft.
10 ft. (width of large projection or video screen)	12 ft.
16 ft.	20 ft. (large conference room)
83 ft.	100 ft. (large hall)

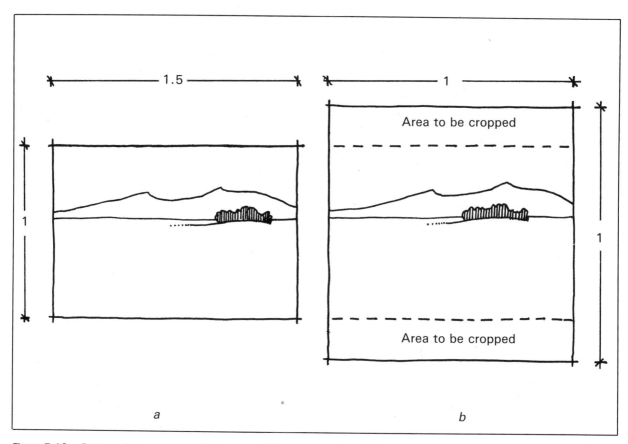

Figure 7-13. Rectangular image proportions: normal 35 mm camera lens (full-frame photograph) (*a*); 2 1/2 × 2 1/2 inch negative from large-format camera (*b*).

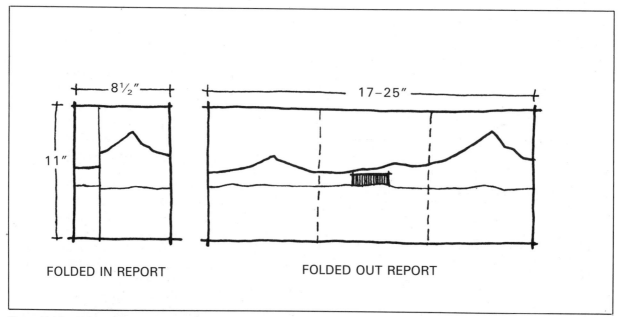

FOLDED IN REPORT   FOLDED OUT REPORT

Figure 7-14. Foldout panoramic simulation.

Figure 7-15. Photosimulation of proposed freeway intersection: Original field of view = 100 degrees (wide-angle lens) (*a*). Correct viewing distance for this image size would be 3.5 inches. Original field of view = 40 degrees (*b*). Correct viewing distance for this image size would be 11 inches.

131

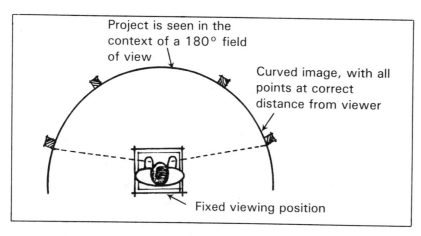

Figure 7-16. Plan view of a 180-degree simulation booth.

Figure 7-17. An example of a well-presented simulation, complete with "before" view and key-map of viewpoint.

outlasting their patience. Rehearse so as to test the timing of the presentation and avoid disruptive logistical problems (such as slides placed upside down, an uncooperative video monitor, or a faulty microphone). Avoid distracting the audience from the subject matter or challenging their belief by too flippant, hasty, or casual a manner.

- When using a packaged presentation, such as slides or video, provide wall graphics of the same views to allow more sustained, informal, and repeat viewing for interpreters.

- Record any comments or criticisms that are made with regard to the simulations or presentation. These are useful in establishing credibility at a later stage, or in revising simulations if necessary. In particular, it is possible at this stage to get an informal appraisal of the representativeness, visual clarity, interest level, and legitimacy of simulations, as well as direct feedback on the credibility and comprehension of the presentation.

GUIDELINES FOR APPRAISING SIMULATIONS, PRECONSTRUCTION

Since the value of simulations lies in predicting the appearance of future environments, it follows that potential problems in their use must be detected and, if possible, eliminated before decisions on project approval are made. The best time for this is before the public or key decision-makers see the simulations (although if this is not possible, appraisal can be used to judge the quality of the actual presentation itself).

The quality of a simulation must at this stage be judged on its own merits, without benefit of comparison with the finished project. How can this be done? How are people to know if a simulation is accurate or misleading? The questions posed below, which respond directly to the principles outlined in Chapter 6, provide criteria for simulation appraisal. Some of these questions are more easily answered than others.

Simulation appraisal would appear to introduce a new step in the project-review process and add to the red tape and administrative burden of regulatory agencies. In fact, an informal version of appraisal already exists, in the shape of agency review of preliminary draft or administrative draft environmental reports (which often

TABLE 7-7. SIMULATION APPRAISAL DATA REQUIREMENTS

1. **Basic Project Data Used to Prepare Simulations**
   Necessary:
   - Description of the project, including structure heights, colors, and materials
   - Site plan(s) or maps preferably including grading, access roads, landscaping, and roofs
   - Project elevations and/or cross sections
   Desirable:
   - Design specifications (if available)
   - Color samples of materials (if appropriate)
   - Design assumptions where design decisions have not yet been made
   - Aerial photograph of site
   - Environmental impact report or other relevant planning/design documents, if available
   - Photographs of similar built projects

2. **Evidence of Simulation Process**
   Necessary:
   - Map(s) showing location of viewpoints and their relationship to the site plan or project features
   - Scale verification techniques, such as photographs of survey poles or other markers used in the field, or reference points surveyed/digitized
   Desirable:
   - Rationale for selection of viewpoints, or accompanying visual analysis carried out in conjunction with simulation process
   - Line-of-sight diagrams (cross sections or profiles of terrain, vegetation, and structures between the viewpoint and the project)
   - Map showing angles of view used in simulations
   - Viewshed maps from viewpoints used in simulation
   - Perspective construction methods and calculations; or computer program used (with cell size and contour interval used for terrain), with source of digital data
   - Preliminary simulations (such as perspective sketches or wire-frame computer perspectives)

3. **Simulation and Presentation Products**
   Necessary:
   - Simulations themselves, preferably in the form(s) in which they will be presented (such as printer's proof or half-tone reproduction)
   - Corresponding photograph(s) or video/film of existing conditions
   Desirable:
   - Description of labels, titles, and other relevant presentation data that will accompany the simulations
   - Potential or unavoidable inaccuracies contained in the simulation (e.g., ''planned future development on adjoining site is not shown because the nature of the development has not yet been decided'')

contain simulations), prior to public release. The guidelines presented here merely provide a more solid framework for those who wish to monitor or control simulation quality.

Table 7-7 provides a list of materials that are either essential or useful for appraising a set of simulations. Much of the basic project data used to prepare simulations is likely to be in the project-application package and therefore may already be in the hands of the reviewing agency.

How Representative of Important Views Are the Simulations?

This can be determined readily by

1. Listing viewpoints where viewers of the real project would be, and the conditions in which they would typically see it (see Appendix A for suggestions on identifying important views). These should be determined by study of maps, consideration of any public or agency concerns that have been expressed regarding sensitive views, and a site visit.
2. Comparing this list to the viewpoints used in the simulations and the conditions depicted. This will reveal important views that have

not been simulated, and unimportant or unrepresentative views that have.

Be suspicious of unusual lighting or viewing conditions depicted in a simulation. Also, watch for too narrow or wide a field-of-view; this is an angle of view or "cone of vision" that includes much less or much more of the view than an observer at the site would be aware of when looking in the same direction (see Fig. 6-3). The field-of-view shown in the simulation, if not already specified, can be found by locating the viewpoint on a map of the project site, and mapping the field-of-view in reference to objects or landmarks that appear near the left and right sides of the simulation image. The steps in this process (as shown in Fig. 7-18) are as follows:

1. Locate the viewpoint on a map.
2. Identify landmarks in the simulation image.
3. Identify the same landmarks on the map, as well as other landmarks that fall just outside the frame of the simulation.
4. Draw radiating lines on the map out from the viewpoint through those landmarks that occur near the left and right sides of the simulation.
5. Estimate where the edges of the simulation field-of-view occur with respect to landmarks, and draw in the radiating lines that form the cone of vision on the map.

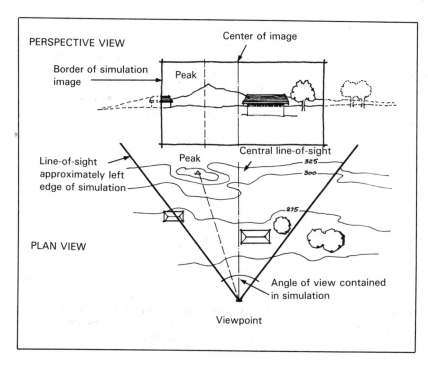

Figure 7-18. Mapping field-of-view in a simulation.

6. Measure the angle of view between the lines forming the cone of vision.

View angles much less than 45 degrees or more than 130 degrees can generally be considered to be unrepresentative (unless there are unusual site characteristics that limit view angles or provide extensive panoramic views).

How Accurate Are the Simulations?

The overall accuracy of a simulation is known with certainty only after the project is built. Hence, we can only predict or estimate accuracy at the time the simulation is used.

Some types of inaccuracy are easier to detect than others:

INACCURACIES THAT ARE OBVIOUS. These are detectable almost at a glance simply by observing the simulation itself. Examples include inaccuracies due to

*   abstraction and use of symbols
*   elaborate or expressive artistic style
*   lack of context, as for example, when the project is seen without a background
*   obvious errors, such as objects appearing to float above the ground, or "sloppy" graphics

INACCURACIES OF CONTENT THAT ARE SIMPLE TO DETECT. These can be found by simple comparison of the simulation with the project description, plans, sections, and so forth. This reveals inaccuracies in subject matter, that is, objects that are omitted from the simulation, wrongly included in it, or present in the wrong numbers. These can be identified by checking the objects mentioned in project information, and present in photographs of the existing site, against objects shown in the simulation. Objects that would be hidden in that particular view should be taken into account. If necessary, lists of project components can be drawn up for systematic comparison (see Appraisal Form 2 in Appendix A).

INACCURACIES OF DISTORTION THAT ARE MORE DIFFICULT TO DETECT. These can be estimated only by a more involved comparison of the simulation with the project description, while visualizing how the viewpoint and viewing conditions would affect project appearance. The inaccuracies concerned include distortion of position, scale, shape, color, texture, and detail of the project or scene.

Gross inaccuracies in these image elements may quickly become apparent, but more subtle (yet potentially misleading) inaccuracies can be hard to predict. Some basic tools exist that can be used by nonexperts to check simulation accuracy. An example is the use of accurately drawn cross sections through topography, trees, and buildings. They can reveal how much of a proposed structure would be screened from view, and the results can then be compared with the simulation (Fig. 7-19). Such line-of-sight profiles can resolve questions of accuracy in the position of objects in the up–down dimension and depth in the picture, as well as questions of relative height. The mapping technique shown in Figure 7-18 can be used to determine roughly whether objects are correctly placed in the left–right dimension. Taking the simulations into the field in a visit to the actual viewpoint may help to identify problems that are not apparent in the simulation itself. See Appendix A for further discussion of techniques to ensure accuracy.

Some indication of accuracy and distortion may be obtained by examining the methods employed by preparers of simulations, for instance, their perspective construction drawings or use of scale markers of the site. If even simple perspective calculations or scale references cannot be produced, then it should be assumed that the scale may be distorted, because guesswork is seldom accurate. If in doubt about the scale of the project or other aspects of the simulation, place the burden of proof on the preparers. Have them prove to you that they are right. Where major questions are unresolved, the skills of a professional planner, designer, or illustrator who is familiar with the use and preparation of visual simulations may be required; this can provide more solid judgments, or even an attempt to repeat the simulation process.

It is important to remember that some types of inaccuracy may be unavoidable. For example, project designs may still be evolving at the time of simulation; or it may be unfeasible to show the effects of motion in simulations of a project where movement is important. Moreover, some inaccuracies may not influence the fairness of the simulation (Table 7-8). Inaccuracies that do not substantially alter the perceived visual im-

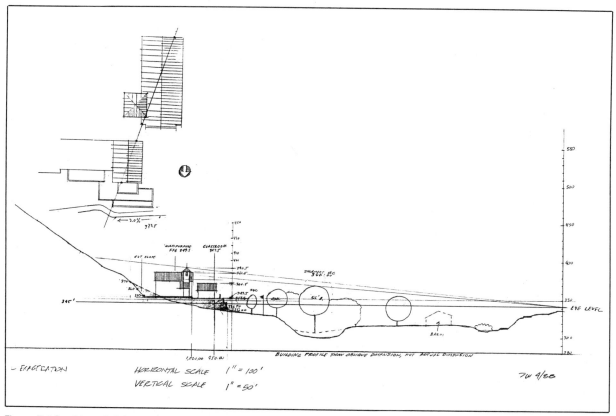

Figure 7-19. Line-of-sight sections used to determine the extent of screening of a proposed building.

pact of a project, for example, are unlikely to present problems in their interpretation for aesthetics. Detecting inaccuracies is only one step in evaluating how misleading or unsatisfactory a simulation may be to users. The fact that inaccuracies have been detected does not automatically invalidate a simulation. What is important is that any such inaccuracies are known and borne in mind at the time the simulations are presented and decisions made.

Note that the accuracy of both generic and specific simulations can be described in relation to either assumed or actual design characteristics. Generic simulations can be as misleading as specific simulations, and should not be absolved from an appraisal of accuracy.

Are the Simulations Visually Clear?

This issue may be resolved directly by observing the reactions and comments of people seeing or interpreting the simulation. However, it is advis-

able and fairly simple to predict these reactions, and so avoid potential problems of skepticism and uncertainty.

Most presentation problems, such as poor focus or an image too small to be seen properly, can be detected readily, although in some cases it may be important to preview not only the simulation itself but also the simulation setting. Graphics that are clear when seen at arm's length may be unintelligible from the back of a room. Similarly, proofs should be reviewed prior to mass printing for public documents.

If there is some doubt about visual clarity, it is a good idea to test the simulation presentation with a small group of people, as a dress rehearsal.

It is important that any lack of clarity in the entire simulation should not be confused with real obscurity of the project. If a project would not be seen clearly in reality—for example, because of tree screening or low color-contrast—it could be misleading to illustrate it with bold clarity. The overall image should remain clear, however.

TABLE 7-8.   POTENTIALLY MISLEADING INACCURACIES

		Favorable Bias	Unfavorable Bias
Content	Objects wrongly included or included in exaggerated numbers	Trees and landscaping Other objects that screen the project People, animals, flags, stylish cars, yachts	Power lines, utility structures Parking lots
	Objects wrongly omitted or too few in number	Power lines and utility structures Parking lots and vehicles	Landscaping and trees Other objects that screen or backdrop the project
Image Elements	Position	Project component(s) located too low or nestled behind screening vegetation	Project component(s) located too high, on skyline, or in front of other features
	Scale	Structure(s) or "hardscape" reduced in scale or extent Landscaping and trees exaggerated in height or extent	Structure(s) or "hardscape" exaggerated in scale or extent
	Color	Reduced color contrasts with setting Bright, light, cheerful colors on project details (in urban setting) and landscaping	Exaggerated color contrast with setting Colors that are too dark, somber, or gray, particularly if monotonous
	Shape/Form/Edges	Structures that are too slender or low in profile Structures and landforms that conform too closely to surrounding natural forms	Structures with exaggerated height, bulk, or breadth Structures, "hardscape," and landforms with exaggerated or overly geometric shapes contrasting with surrounding natural forms
	Texture/Detail	Exaggerated amount of texture and detail on blank facades or surfaces	Omission of texture and detail on surfaces and foreground

How Interesting Are the Simulations?

Again, this issue is best resolved by reviewing and rehearsing the presentation, preferably with staff who can represent the potential audience. Sometimes the preparers' familiarity with the simulation makes it hard to judge the interest level on first or second encounter. If professional staff become bored on their first viewing, then lay people are almost certain to be bored by that stage in the process.

Presentations that are too entertaining should be viewed with suspicion and toned down to be neutral and more informative.

How Defensible Are the Simulations?

The legitimacy of simulations can be appraised by checking the following points:

- The preparers have documented their methods, calculations, and assumptions.
- A rationale is provided for selecting views and viewpoints.
- Views of the existing site, preliminary simulations, and graphic scale verifications (such as site photos with scale markers) are available for presentation.

The credibility of the preparer with the intended audience should also be taken into account in weighing legitimacy.

It should be noted that the characteristics described in the preceding sections do not always correspond with those that may be singled out for praise or criticism by the public, or indeed by environmental professionals who rely on intuition and a cursory inspection of the simulation. As an example, a simulation that is well accepted and lauded for its realism may in fact contain major inaccuracies in scale, content, and so forth. People tend to confuse precision or ''realism'' with accuracy. Hence, the high credibility of a simulation, without an evaluation of other factors such as its accuracy and choice of viewpoints, does not assure its fairness. However, the low credibility of a simulation usually does indicate that problems exist, with the potential for bias.

The point at which potentially misleading or unsatisfactory aspects of a simulation become serious enough to warrant action by the appraiser must be decided case by case. The person appraising or screening the simulation must take into account the users' experience with simulations, the importance of the visual issue in project approval, and the consequences of a biased or disputed decision. In general, if it is believed that simulations are markedly unrepresentative, are likely to be misunderstood or criticized by users, are very inaccurate in a single important aspect, or contain several potentially misleading inaccuracies (see Table 7-8), the simulations should be rejected and new or revised versions requested. Beware, in particular, of severe abstraction, distortions of contrast between project and setting, stylistic rendering by commercial illustrators who are used to preparing sales drawings, and black-and-white photomontage of blank building silhouettes as used in massing studies (see also the discussion of the causes of accuracy problems in Chapter 6).

Appendix A provides two possible formats that can be used to structure and record the appraisal. The first is a one-page checklist that can be checked off quickly to determine whether or not simulations are acceptable. This form would be appropriate for routine project submittals with simulations, or where visual issues are not particularly critical. The second format consists of a two-page form that provides for a more thorough and detailed appraisal of both the total simulation package and each simulation image. This format would be more appropriate for large or controversial projects where aesthetic issues are critical, or where the validity of simulations is likely to be questioned. Chapter 8 demonstrates how these forms may be used, with case-study examples of simulation appraisals. The forms are intended to allow a comprehensive review of simulation quality. Agencies wishing to carry out simulation appraisals can modify or simplify these forms to suit their own special needs.

GUIDELINES FOR APPRAISING SIMULATIONS, POSTCONSTRUCTION

Following up on simulations in comparison with the real views after a project is built provides the most complete appraisal of their validity in terms of representation and accuracy. (Clarity, interest, and legitimacy can all be determined at the presentation stage and will not be discussed here.) The criteria used to appraise representation and accuracy after construction are similar to those used before construction, though simpler to apply. In addition, however, the built project also provides a means of directly measuring the bias in simulations, as described below.

The key to postconstruction appraisal of both simulations and projects is, of course, a site visit to compare predicted and as-built conditions. This requires taking simulations into the field, in a suitably portable and robust form. Conversely, if simulations cannot be taken to the field, as with a large model or video sequence requiring audiovisual equipment, the corresponding actual views should be recorded by photography or video for comparison in the office. In either case, make sure that the simulations being evaluated are in the format that was used in making decisions or that received public attention; this may be in black-and-white, cropped, report format rather than the original simulations, which may have full color and a wider angle of view but which may not have been seen by most people.

The two-page form for appraising simulations given in Appendix A is also useful here in responding to the questions in the following section.

How Representative of Important Views Are the Simulations?

This can be determined by the following steps:

1. Visit the site and drive or walk around on surrounding roads, public rights-of-way, and other viewer locations. This will quickly give you a feeling for the visibility of the project. Can it be seen easily from many angles and locations? Which are the most important and representative of the various viewing locations?
2. What effects do season, lighting, and maturity of landscaping have on the views, and are they significant in affecting the visual and design qualities of the project? (See also the section below on selecting appropriate time and conditions for the site visit.)

3. Identify on the ground, if possible, the precise viewpoints used in the simulations. This can be very difficult if the viewpoint has not been well documented or marked. You may need to use the simulation itself to get into a position where the real and simulated views match up. Take into account plant growth, road widenings, and other changes that may have occurred in the intervening years. Map the precise viewpoints. How well do they match up with the viewpoints you have identified as being important?
4. At each viewpoint, photograph the actual view and compare the view direction and field-of-view in the simulation with that on-site. How well do they represent what you actually see? Are the viewing conditions shown in the simulation typical or unusual?

How Accurate Are the Simulations?

This question can be answered readily by following these steps:

1. Each simulation image can be compared directly with its corresponding real view to appraise its accuracy. In particular, at this stage it becomes easy to identify differences in both content and image elements (scale, color, and so forth) between the real and simulated scenes (see the third case study in the following chapter). It is important, however, to match the viewing conditions assumed in the simulation with those prevailing during the site visit, where possible. For example, it is not completely fair to contrast a simulation showing backlit conditions in a snowy winter scene with a site visit in summer under conditions of frontlighting and heat haze, if the simulated conditions are equally typical and representative.
2. Identify viewing conditions (lighting, season, weather) shown in the simulation. These should be documented already by the preparer of the simulations, but if not, they can be estimated by reference to clues in the simulation, such as shadow directions, amount and color of foliage, and sky and visibility conditions.
3. Conduct the site visits to the precise viewpoints as described in the preceding series of

steps, under conditions as similar as possible to those identified in the simulations.

4. List project components and other major features of the real scene that are most noticeable. Compare this with the visual content of the simulation. Have objects or features been omitted from the simulation, wrongly included in the simulation, or included in the wrong quantity?

5. Compare the simulation image with the real scene. Is the project located in the same place with respect to the landscape in both views? Is the project scale correctly simulated in relation to its setting (not necessarily in terms of overall image size)? Are the shapes, colors, textures, and details of project components similar to those simulated?

6. Overall, are the visual impact and design quality of the actual project similar to or significantly different from the project as simulated?

7. If significant discrepancies occur in either content or image elements, determine the cause. In particular, is it due to simulation inaccuracy, to a change in project design after the simulation was created, or to improper construction technique? This can be ascertained by comparing (a) design documents and assumptions used at the time of simulation and (b) later design documents, required mitigation treatments, or as-built drawings and specifications. Radical design changes may be obvious without such a review. Where comparison of project plans is required, good documentation of the simulation data base again makes it much easier to get to the bottom of the problem.

Based on these appraisals, the overall quality of the simulations and the likelihood of decisions being biased can be judged (see Table 7-8 for potentially misleading inaccuracies).

However, as mentioned, it is also possible to measure the amount and direction of bias in people's responses to simulations by comparing their reactions to the real project with reactions to the simulations. This has been termed the *response equivalence* of simulations. It can be measured either informally or with full scientific rigor.

Informal appraisals of bias can be obtained by

- asking a group of people to review simulations of a project together with supporting information, and to record their feelings (positive or negative) about the project
- taking them to the site and asking them to record their feelings on seeing the real project
- comparing the two sets of information

It is possible (and easier) to show photographs or video of the real project instead of organizing a site visit, so long as the viewpoints are truly representative and correspond to the simulated viewing conditions. It is also possible simply to ask people to compare actual and simulated views side-by-side (via site visits or photography) and to tell you if they feel differently about the two scenes. However, the author's research suggests that direct side-by-side comparisons may exaggerate the perceived differences between real and simulated views, and do not necessarily correlate well with bias measured by more valid techniques.

The difficulty with informal measurement of response bias is that it is difficult to get objective results. More formal scientific methods achieve this by using large samples of people who ideally have no knowledge of or harbor no preconceived ideas about the built project, and who can be tested under carefully controlled conditions to avoid spurious results. In fact, the correct way to measure response equivalence between real and simulated scenes is to use two equivalent groups of people and ask one group to respond to the real scene while the other group responds to the simulations. Then the two independent sets of responses can be compared without fear that viewing the simulations first may have affected people's responses to the real scene (or vice versa). This approach, as used in the author's study and others, may be feasible in practice and is recommended for postconstruction evaluation of large projects such as controversial power lines or offshore oil rigs along scenic coastlines, where debate about aesthetic and related impacts runs high. For most projects, however, it is beyond the scope of normal agency budgets and is likely to remain an academic research tool.

REFERENCES

1. Appleyard, D. 1977. ''Understanding professional media.'' In *Human Behavior and Environment,* Vol. 1, ed. Altman and Wohlwill, New York: Plenum Press, pp. 43–88.

2. Danahy, J. W., and R. Wright. 1988. ''Exploring design through 3-dimensional simulations.'' *Landscape Architecture* 78(5):64–71.

3. Orland, B. 1988. ''Video imaging: a powerful tool for visualization and analysis.'' *Landscape Architecture* 78(5):78–88.

4. Sheppard, S. R. J., and T. Tetherow. 1983. ''Visual assessment of surface mining in the Alton Coalfield: Bryce Canyon, Utah.'' *Garten & Landschaft* 8(83):624–28.

Chapter **8**

CASE STUDIES
IN SIMULATION APPRAISAL

This chapter provides examples of how to go about appraising simulation quality, and what can happen as a result. It shows how simulation appraisal forms can be used to develop, record, and justify an agency's decision on the adequacy of simulations for a specific project. It also illustrates the type of materials and information that a regulatory agency can or should expect from the preparer when simulations are crucial to project approval.

Three examples have been chosen:

1. Preconstruction appraisal of a relatively unsophisticated simulation for a hypothetical project.
2. Preconstruction appraisal of a relatively sophisticated set of simulations used on an actual project.
3. Postconstruction appraisal of photosimulations used on an actual project.

In all cases, the appraisals have been carried out by the author in the same way that an agency reviewer might use the suggested appraisal forms.

Obviously, three examples cannot illustrate every major issue in simulation appraisal. Consult

Chapter 6 for other common problems to watch for in simulation appraisal.

CASE STUDY: PRECONSTRUCTION APPRAISAL OF A RENDERING OF A HOUSING DEVELOPMENT

Background to the Simulation

This hypothetical project is a planned unit development in a scenic coastal zone.* The simulation, a single black-and-white rendering (Fig. 8-1), has been prepared to show the local Planning Commission what the design will look like in a meeting at which an environmental study (prepared by the applicant) will be presented. The study report is brief and contains no specific visual analysis, other than a general description

---

*This case study is purely hypothetical and is intended only to illustrate some of the more common problems encountered by project reviewers using simulations anywhere. All names used in this case study are fictitious, and no resemblance to any actual project, developer, simulation preparer, or review agency is intended.

Figure 8-1. Rendering of proposed Stagshead Planned Unit Development (hypothetical).

of impacts on land-use and open-space and a commitment to ''blend the development into its surroundings with landscape plantings and earth-tone colors.'' There have been other recent projects approved nearby, and some have been criticized on aesthetic grounds by local residents and environmental interest groups, who charge that the appearance of these developments is not compatible with the coastal zone regulations.

In addition to the report, materials available to the review agency from the applicant include

- Photograph of existing site from a similar viewpoint (Fig. 8-2)
- Conceptual site plan (Fig. 8-3)
- Typical elevations (Fig. 8-4)

The Appraisal

The simulation appraisal checklist, as filled out by a reviewer, is given next (Fig. 8-5), together with a quick line-of-sight diagram (Fig. 8-6) that

Figure 8-2. Photograph of existing conditions.

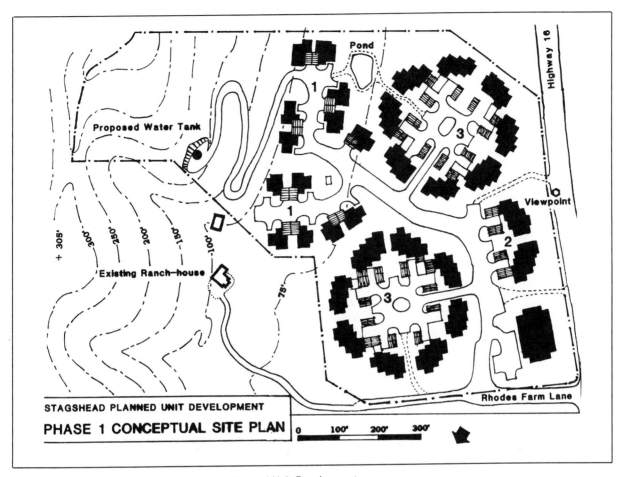

Figure 8-3. Conceptual site plan, Stagshead Planned Unit Development.

Figure 8-4. Typical elevations, Stagshead Planned Unit Development.

SIMULATION APPRAISAL CHECKLIST

PROJECT: STAGSHEAD P.U.D.
LOCATION: STAGSHEAD, CALIFORNIA
APPLICANT: ENTERPRISES INC.
PREPARER OF SIMULATIONS: GRAPHO DESIGNS
PREPARATION DATE: 5/87

REVIEW DATE: 8/29/87
REVIEWER: J. EVERYMAN

1 REPRESENTATIVENESS

	YES	NO	COMMENTS
a) Are the following important views included?			
_1._ View from Coastal Hwy.	✓		⎫ Similar view direction
_2._ From nearby homes		X	⎬ as shown in 1.
_3._ From scenic trail		X	⎭
_____			
_____			
_____			
b) Are all the simulated views important or typical?	✓		
c) Are typical or important viewing conditions shown?	✓	X	Shown with mature trees; earlier project phases not shown

2 ACCURACY

	YES	NO	COMMENTS
a) Are simulations free of obvious inaccuracies?		X	Pronounced "sketchy" style: no values/shading; inadequate detail
b) Do simulations show correct and adequate project context?		?	Hills not clearly shown
c) Do simulations include all project components which would be visible?		X	Omits access road, pad, and water tank on hillside
d) Do all the objects shown in the simulations conform with site plans and applicable regulations?	✓		Building details hard to determine
e) Do simulations appear accurate in position, scale and shape of project?		X	Building scale/roof height seems too low (see attached line-of-sight diagram)
f) Do simulations appear accurate in color and important project details?		X	Impossible to tell

3 VISUAL CLARITY

	YES	NO	COMMENTS
Are simulations visually clear and understandable?	✓		

4 INTEREST

	YES	NO	COMMENTS
Are simulations interesting without being overly entertaining?	✓		

5 LEGITIMACY

	YES	NO	COMMENTS
a) Is a supporting visual analysis provided?		X	
b) Are viewpoints mapped?	✓		
c) Are project design data and assumptions documented?		X	No landscape plan referenced No assumptions of age of landscaping
d) Are "before" photographs provided?	✓		
e) Are scale and location verifications provided?		X	

6 RECOMMENDATIONS

Accept ___ **Add** ___
Revise ___ **Reject** ___

PROVIDE A MORE ACCURATE & DETAILED SIMULATION AS OVERLAY TO PHOTO-SHOW ARCHITECTURAL DETAIL, WATER TOWER & GRADING, TONAL VALUES, & ACCURATE LANDSCAPING

Figure 8-5. Simulation appraisal checklist for Stagshead Planned Unit Development.

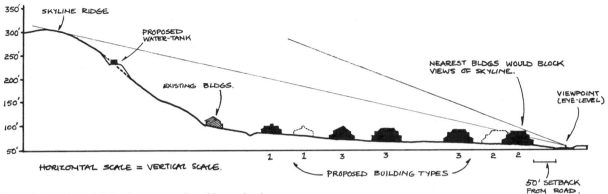

Figure 8-6. Line-of-sight diagram produced by reviewing agency.

the agency produces as part of its appraisal. This diagram shows that buildings, as located in the plan, would obstruct the skyline in this view and appear larger or taller than those shown in the rendering.

The appraisal reveals that the simulation does not represent important views from nearby residences, and is too sketchy and stylized to give a clear impression of the project's relationship to its context. Important features of the project, such as the water tank on the hill above, are omitted. The simulation is potentially misleading due to inaccuracies in scale and lack of information (or stated assumptions) on architecture and landscaping. It is unlikely to resolve uncertainties in the minds of its audience regarding the project's design quality, and may be seen by some members of the public as an attempt by the developer to cover up the true impacts of the project.

Based on their appraisal, the local agency staff clearly feel that the rendering, with relatively little supporting information, does not provide an adequate basis for their recommendation or the Planning Commission's decision on the aesthetic compatibility of the project with its setting. The staff recommend that the project application be rejected on grounds of inadequacy, and that the schedule be set back approximately six weeks while two new and more credible simulations are prepared. They also recommend that the applicant modify the site plan to increase setbacks from the road and nearby residences, thus reducing obstruction of the ridges.

Discussion

In this hypothetical scenario, the checklists provide the agency staff with a consistent set of criteria and specific recommendations that the applicant can follow in bringing the application materials up to par. The applicant cannot complain of being unfairly treated, since all other developments in the coastal zone undergo the same simulation appraisal process. Through the appraisal, it has been discovered that the project could significantly impact important skyline views. Consequently, the site plans are altered and the changed design is reflected in the new simulations, which meet with agency, Planning Commission, and general public acceptance. The developer has lost time due to an inadequate first submittal, but, through the appraisal and resimulation process, he has retained his credibility with the local community. His project eventually is approved with specific design controls to ensure that the agency's requirements are met.

This example, although entirely fictitious, does represent an amalgamation of typical everyday problems in simulation use, together with potential solutions. The appraisal process could just as easily have shown that the simulation overstated project impacts and, thus, have saved both the applicant and the agency considerable time and trouble in arguing over problems that do not really exist.

CASE STUDY: PRECONSTRUCTION APPRAISAL OF SIMULATIONS OF A TRANSMISSION LINE

Background to the Simulation

This project, the Austrop-McNeil 345 kv transmission line in Austin, Texas, is an example of an urban siting study for utility lines. The municipality needed to bring electrical power into an existing substation that is close to homes, churches, and parkland. As part of the city approval process, alternative transmission line routes into the substation were considered in order to select the best route in terms of environmental impact and cost. Photosimulations, supported by computer graphics, were prepared to aid the environmental assessment, and to show the local people in public workshops what the relative merits of the alternative routes were.

Materials provided to the city and the public by the consultants conducting the studies include

- Existing photographs and photosimulations of three proposed project alternatives, from six key viewpoints (Figs. 8-7–8-12 and Plate 30)

- Overall corridor map showing the alternatives (Fig. 8-13)
- Computer-graphic overlays to the photographs, showing the location and scale of proposed transmission line towers (example shown in Fig. 8-14)
- Specifications for transmission line structures (Fig. 8-15)
- Information on heights of specific towers
- Visual analysis describing how the viewpoints were picked, and interpretation of the results.[1]
- Specifications for tree heights, species, and density for use in screening views of transmission lines

Appraisal forms, as they might have been completed by a hypothetical reviewer prior to releasing the simulations, are included as Figure 8-16.

a

b

Figure 8-7. ''Before'' (*a*) and ''after'' (*b*) of power line Link 5 seen though the window of Christ Sanctuary, Brentwood Church.

a

b

Figure 8-8. "Before" (*a*) and "after" (*b*) of power line Link 5 seen from the Christ Chapel window of Brentwood Church.

a

b

Figure 8-9. "Before" (*a*) and "after" (*b*) of power line Link 3 seen from a nearby residential area.

Figure 8-10. "Before" (a) and "after" (b) of power line Link 3 adjacent to residential properties.

Figure 8-11. "Before" (a) and "after" (b) of power line Link 8 seen from Walnut Creek Metropolitan Park.

a

b

Figure 8-12. "Before" (*a*) and "after" (*b*) Link 8 seen from entrance bridge at Walnut Creek Metropolitan Park.

Key: → 8–12 indicates viewpoint used in Figure 8–12.

Figure 8-13. Corridor map of transmission-line alternatives (links) and viewpoints used in Figures 8-7 through 8-12.

151

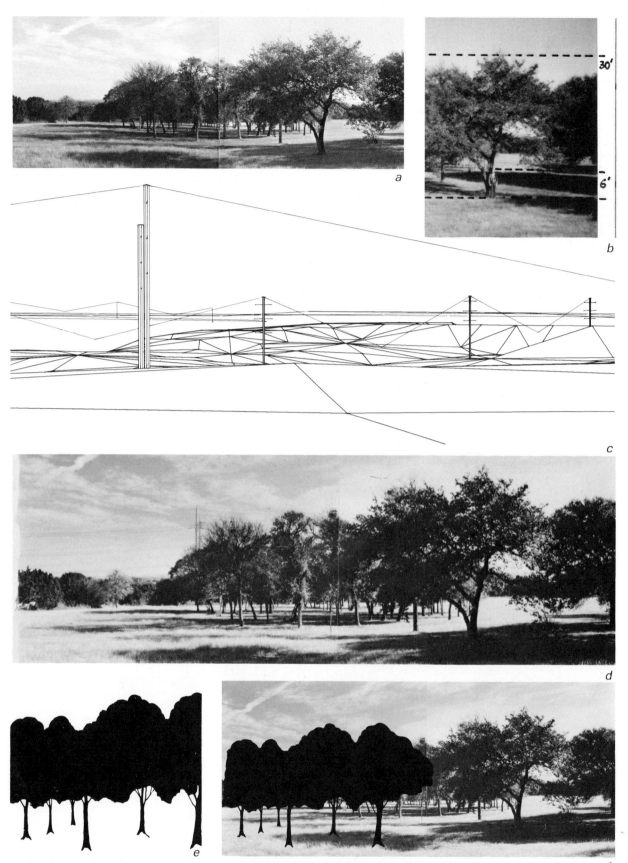

Figure 8-14. Example of simulation process: existing scene (panoramic view) (*a*); part of existing scene with person for height reference (*b*); computer perspective of proposed towers (*c*); photosimulation of proposed towers (*d*); overlay sketch with proposed tree screening (*e*); overlay sketch superimposed on photosimulation (*f*).

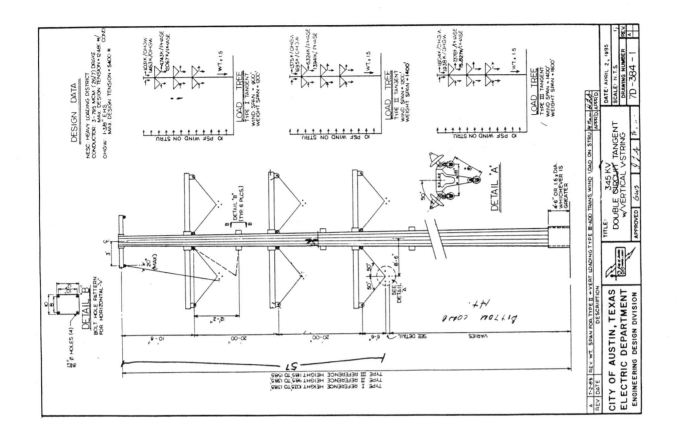

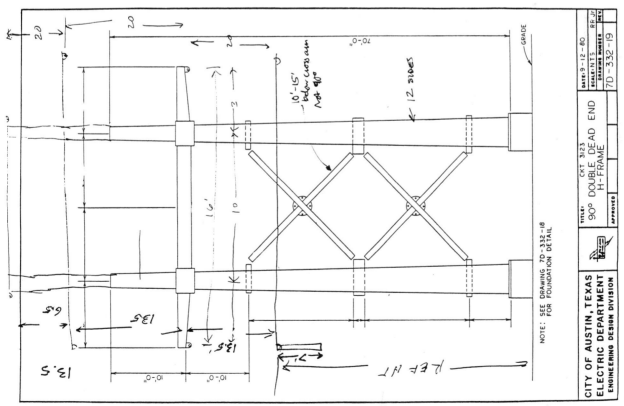

Figure 8-15. Specifications for transmission-line structures.

153

SIMULATION APPRAISAL FORM 1   _1_ OF _2_

PRE-CONSTRUCTION _X_	DATE: 5 SEPT. 1987
POST-CONSTRUCTION ___	REVIEWER: J. SMITH

PROJECT: *AUSTROP-MACNEIL POWERLINE*
LOCATION: *AUSTIN, TEXAS*
APPLICANT: *CITY OF AUSTIN*
PROJECT REVIEW STAGE:

SUPPORTING VISUAL ANALYSIS: YES ✓ NO ___

PREPARER: *DAMES & MOORE*
DATE OF SIMULATION: *1986*
ACCOMPANYING DATA: *CORRIDOR MAPS, VIEWPOINT MAPS, COMPUTER PERSPECTIVES, LANDSCAPE SCREENING PERSPECTIVES*
PRESENTATION FORMAT:
Report ___
Meeting ✓ *PUBLIC WORKSHOPS*

1 REPRESENTATIVENESS	SIMU-LATION #	YES	NO	COMMENTS
1.1 Are the following important views included*: A View through main church window (sanctuary) B View from chapel window C Close-up view from adjoining properties D View from residential area E View from Walnut Creek park F Focal view along creek from park bridge —	1 2 3 4 5 6 —	✓ ✓ ✓ ✓ ✓ ✓		*1 and 2. Church view points specifically requested by church members* *5. Appears to be worst-case* *6. Needed to establish if line is visible here.*
1.2 Are unimportant or unrepresentative views included: — —	— —		✓	

	N/A	YES	NO	
1.3 Are typical or important viewing conditions represented: i Project phases or maturity ii Season/weather/lighting iii Field-of-view iv View sequence/duration v Mitigated project vi Project alternatives		✓ ✓ ✓ ✓ ✓		*Simulations assume retention of healthy trees. Views 1 & 2 show with & without screening* *Panoramas included* *Most views are of long duration not sequential road views* *Overlays of tree planting*

	GOOD	MAR-GINAL	POOR	RECOMMENDATION:
1.4 Overall representativeness:	✓			

2 VISUAL INTEREST	GOOD	MAR-GINAL	POOR	RECOMMENDATION:
Are the simulations too lengthy, brief, repetitive, numerous, overly entertaining:	✓			

3 LEGITIMACY	GOOD	MAR-GINAL	POOR	RECOMMENDATION:
Is the simulation process defensible and documented: i "Before" photographs provided* ii Project design data documented iii Viewpoints mapped* iv Scale verifications provided* v Assumptions documented vi Other:	✓ ✓ ✓ ✓	✓		*Referred to in report*

* Checking a "No" or "Poor" in these categories normally precludes acceptance of simulation.

Figure 8-16. Simulation appraisal forms for Austrop-McNeil Powerline, Austin, Texas.

SIMULATION APPRAISAL FORM 2

PROJECT: *AUSTROP-MACNEIL TRANSMISSION*

4 | ACCURACY

		1	2	3	4	5	6	COMMENTS
4.1	**Do simulations contain obvious inaccuracies:**	Ok	Ok	Ok	Ok	Ok	Ok	*Supporting computer perspectives show severe abstraction Also, screening diagrams*
i	Severe abstraction*							
ii	Pronounced style							
iii	Obvious errors							
4.2	**Do simulations show incorrect or inadequate project context:**	Ok	Ok	Ok	Ok	Ok	Ok	
4.3	**Do simulations omit or contain incorrect project components:**							
i	Buildings							
ii	Walls/fences							
iii	Roads/paving/parking							
iv	Grading (cut & fill)							
v	Vegetation removal			Ok	Ok			*Trees cut back in views 3 & 4*
vi	Landscaping - foreground	Ok	Ok					
vii	Landscaping - project area							
viii	Utilities	Ok	Ok	Ok	Ok	Ok	Ok	
ix	Signs							
x	Equipment/vehicles							
xi	People/animals							
xii	Water bodies/features							
xiii	Dust/steam/air emissions							
xiv	Glare/lights/shadows	?	?	?	?	?	?	*Glare from conductor wires?*
xv	Other: _____							
	_____							
	_____							
4.4	**Do simulations show incorrect:**							
i	Position of project							
ii	Scale of project *							*Apparently Ok*
iii	Shape/ mass/ outline of project							
iv	Color (value, chroma, hue) of project							
v	Important details/ textures							
vi	Other:							

RECOMMENDATION: *Full photo simulation of proposed mitigations in 1 & 2 would be helpful, but not essential*

4.5 Overall accuracy:

	1	2	3	4	5	6
GOOD	✓	✓	✓	✓	✓	✓
MARGINAL						
POOR						

5 | VISUAL CLARITY

Are simulations clearly presented:

	1	2	3	4	5	6
GOOD	✓	✓	✓	✓	✓	✓
MARGINAL						
POOR						

RECOMMENDATION:

6 | RECOMMENDED ACTION

	1	2	3	4	5	6
ACCEPT	✓	✓	✓	✓	✓	✓
REVISE						
REJECT						
REPLACE						

ADDITIONAL SIMULATIONS REQUIRED:

155

The Appraisal

This case study represents a detailed simulation effort consistent with a potentially unpopular project in an attractive urban area. Care was taken to select the most critical views for each of the three main alternative routes, and to give each alternative equal consideration. The consultants worked with the local community to identify viewpoints of most concern to them, even to the point of simulating views through the principle windows of a nearby church. Our hypothetical reviewer is satisfied with the choice and breadth of viewpoints used and the supporting documentation.

Accuracy also appears to be high, although some doubts are raised about the precision of the computer graphics since the site topography to be digitized is subtle and vegetation obscures many features normally used for registering computer plots to photographs. Our reviewer is impressed by the computer perspectives, however, and notes that the preparers also cross-checked scale accuracy by estimating tree heights (Fig. 8-14b). Since the computer plots are presented only as support for the final precise photosimulations, there is no problem with abstraction. The mitigation overlay showing tree-planting in views from the church (Fig. 8-14e, f) would have been more convincing in a less abstract form but, given the simulation effort already expended and the ease with which the mitigation solution can be understood, the reviewer does not press for further work. The package is declared adequate, and is even held up as a precedent for other simulation studies to follow.

Discussion

These simulations actually were used in community workshops and were instrumental in selecting the preferred route, which followed Link 5.[1] The simulations were fully accepted by the agency and members of the public who saw them, and clearly communicated the relative impacts of the alternatives. They also lent credibility to the supporting environmental studies. The project has since been put on hold due to a City Council ruling (unrelated to aesthetics) governing all 345 kv transmission lines.

CASE STUDY: POSTCONSTRUCTION APPRAISAL OF PHOTOSIMULATIONS OF A POWER PLANT

Background to the Simulation

This project, the Bottle Rock Geothermal Powerplant in California, was designed and built as a demonstration project. It occurs in a fairly scenic area with considerable tourism value and nearby retirement and second-home communities. The appearance of the project had been identified as a potential issue, and special studies were commissioned to develop an appropriate architectural design and to evaluate its visual impact.[2] As part of this process, black-and-white photosimulations were prepared to help review the designs and assess impacts from key viewpoints. Both photographs of existing conditions (Fig. 8-17) and the photosimulations (Fig. 8-18) were included in the visual analysis report, together with viewpoint location maps.

The Appraisal

Appraisal forms, completed by the author after revisiting the site to photograph the built project (Fig. 8-19 and Plate 31), are included as Figure 8-20. Form 2 (Fig. 8-20), addressing accuracy and clarity, has been filled out for this view only (corresponding to Fig. 8-18b), since it offers the principal opportunity for detailed appraisal.

In this case, the project was obviously built largely as planned, following the design guidelines established for the project. The simulation preparer also did a reasonable job of predicting the building's appearance, although, given the difficulties of estimating elevations and tree heights on the original undisturbed site, a more reliable job of positioning and scale calculation should have been done, using balloons, prominent ground markers, or computer perspectives. As it is, small differences in scale and location can be seen in Figures 8-18b and 8-19 (although slight differences in the elevation of the viewpoint also need to be taken into account—see below). Also, some differences in visibility of grad-

a

b

c

Figure 8-17. Photographs of existing conditions: view from road three miles to the north (*a*); view from opposite hillside half a mile away (*b*); view from state highway, two and a half miles away to the east (*c*).

157

a

b

Figure 8-18. Black-and-white photo-simulations of the proposed Bottle Rock Geothermal Power Plant: view from road to the north (*a*); view from opposite hillside (*b*).

Figure 8-19. Photograph of actual project, taken from a viewpoint close to that in Figure 8-18*b*

SIMULATION APPRAISAL FORM 1 1 OF 2

PRE-CONSTRUCTION ___	DATE: 8/30/85
POST-CONSTRUCTION ✓	REVIEWER:

PROJECT: BOTTLE ROCK GEOTHERMAL PLANT
LOCATION: LAKE COUNTY, CALIFORNIA
APPLICANT: DEPARTMENT OF WATER RESOURCES
PROJECT REVIEW STAGE: Simulations
prepared during final design, after EIR

SUPPORTING VISUAL ANALYSIS: YES ✓ NO ___

PREPARER: S. SHEPPARD
DATE OF SIMULATION: 1981
ACCOMPANYING DATA:
Visual Report with elevations, site plan
PRESENTATION FORMAT:
Report ✓
Meeting _____

1 REPRESENTATIVENESS	SIMU-LATION #	YES	NO	COMMENTS
1.1 Are the following important views included*:				
A	—			
B (Other simulations not appraised)	—			
C	—			
D	—			
E	—			
F	—			
—	—			
—				
1.2 Are unimportant or unrepresentative views included:				
— Overview from hills opposite– view west.	3	✓		Only viewpoint showing design of the whole project
—	—			

1.3 Are typical or important viewing conditions represented:	N/A	YES	NO	
i Project phases or maturity		✓		Shown after graded slopes reclaimed; no major land-scaping would be installed.
ii Season/weather/lighting		✓		
iii Field-of-view		✓		
iv View sequence/duration		✓		
v Mitigated project	✓			
vi Project alternatives	✓			

1.4 Overall representativeness:	GOOD	MAR-GINAL	POOR	RECOMMENDATION:
	✓			////////////

2 **VISUAL INTEREST**	GOOD	MAR-GINAL	POOR	RECOMMENDATION:
Are the simulations too lengthy, brief, repetitive, numerous, overly entertaining:	✓			////////////

3 **LEGITIMACY**	GOOD	MAR-GINAL	POOR	RECOMMENDATION:
Is the simulation process defensible and documented:				
i "Before" photographs provided*	✓			Precise locations not well documented. Scale calculations should have been reviewed at time of simulation.
ii Project design data documented	✓			
iii Viewpoints mapped*		✓		
iv Scale verifications provided*			✓	
v Assumptions documented		✓		
vi Other:				

* Checking a "No" or "Poor" in these categories normally precludes acceptance of simulation.

Figure 8-20. Simulation appraisal forms for Bottle Rock Geothermal Power Plant, Lake County, California (continued on next page).

SIMULATION APPRAISAL FORM 2

PROJECT: *BOTTLE ROCK GEOTHERMAL PLANT*

4 ACCURACY

		SIMULATION #						COMMENTS
		1	2	③	4	5	6	

4.1 Do simulations contain obvious inaccuracies:
i Severe abstraction*
ii Pronounced style
iii Obvious errors

→ Ok (under Simulation 3)

4.2 Do simulations show incorrect or inadequate project context:

→ Ok — *Some other new developments have encroached on the setting.*

4.3 Do simulations omit or contain incorrect project components:
(i) Buildings — Ok
(ii) Walls/fences
(iii) Roads/paving/parking — Ok
(iv) Grading (cut & fill) — X — *Cuts appear too visible*
(v) Vegetation removal — Ok
vi Landscaping - foreground
vii Landscaping - project area
(viii) Utilities — Ok
ix Signs
x Equipment/vehicles
xi People/animals
xii Water bodies/features
(xiii) Dust/steam/air emissions — Ok — *Assuming plant operation*
xiv Glare/lights/shadows
xv Other:

4.4 Do simulations show incorrect:
i Position of project — X — *Elevation differs somewhat*
ii Scale of project * — Ok
iii Shape/mass/outline of project — Ok — *Color simulations would have been helpful*
iv Color (value, chroma, hue) of project — X
v Important details/textures — Ok
vi Other:

4.5 Overall accuracy:

	1	2	3	4	5	6	RECOMMENDATION:
GOOD			✓				
MARGINAL							
POOR							

5 VISUAL CLARITY

Are simulations clearly presented:

	1	2	3	4	5	6	RECOMMENDATION:
GOOD			✓				
MARGINAL							
POOR							

6 RECOMMENDED ACTION *with hindsight:*

Simulation does not seem to be very misleading

	1	2	3	4	5	6	ADDITIONAL SIMULATIONS REQUIRED:
ACCEPT			✓				*Back-up information on scale verification should have been requested at the time*
REVISE							
REJECT							
REPLACE							

Figure 8-20. *(continued)*

160

ing occurs. Overall, however, the visual impacts of the development from this viewpoint appear to be similar in both real and simulated views (assuming that the operating plant would emit steam plumes). Color simulations would have been preferable in evaluating the compatibility of architectural color schemes.

Discussion

Postconstruction appraisal of simulations can shed interesting light on three issues: (1) performance of those responsible for building the project, (2) performance of those preparing the simulations at the time, and (3) performance of those reviewing or using simulations at the time, in terms of their ability to spot problems with the simulations.

With regard to the latter issue, had the simulations undergone any sort of formal review at the time, the client or agency would have been wise to ask for more proof of accuracy in scale and location of project components. Without that, they could not know whether the simulation was accurate in these key elements. Luckily, their faith in the preparer was more or less justi-

fied in this case, but they could equally well have had a nasty shock when the project was built.

Carrying out the postconstruction appraisal for this project reveals the difficulties such an exercise can encounter. Even with the simulation in hand, it proved very difficult to locate the correct original viewpoint, due to irregular terrain and obstructive plant growth. However, this was in part because the view originally was chosen to give an overall impression of the project design, and not to represent views from a major use area. One of the benefits of using typical viewpoints is that it is often easier to obtain access and more precisely locate the point itself.

REFERENCES

1. Dames & Moore. 1987. Environmental Assessment Report, Austrop to McNeil 345 kv Circuit Route Review and Siting Study. Prepared for the City of Austin.

2. Keoseyan, Seyfarth & Associates. 1979. "Visual Evaluation of Bottle Rock Geothermal Powerplant." Report prepared for the California Department of Water Resources.

Chapter 9

POLICIES ON SIMULATION

This chapter suggests ways in which the guidelines on preparation, presentation, and appraisal of simulations can be implemented to improve the quality and consistency of simulations used in project planning. Implementation strategies considered include (1) government regulations and policies encouraging consistent and appropriate use of simulation, and (2) professional standards for use of simulation generally.

GOVERNMENT POLICY ON SIMULATION

Cities, counties, and national or regional agencies that regulate land use stand to gain considerably from using good simulations in decision-making. Rather than taking a passive stance on this issue or reacting in a case-by-case ad hoc fashion, they can exert a strong influence either by encouraging or requiring the preparation of simulations as part of project approval, or by actively participating in preparing simulations themselves. The benefit to applicants is that they know exactly what conditions and requirements they must meet, and can plan ahead accordingly.

Regulations and Guidelines for Project Applicants

An agency can officially adopt a set of guidelines such as those described in Chapter 7. As such, it can formally require project proponents in certain situations to have simulations prepared in a manner that conforms to these guidelines. Appendix C provides a model ordinance and an abbreviated set of guidelines that could be used or adapted by many agencies to enact this requirement under certain well-defined circumstances.

Examples of these circumstances might include projects located in (or visible from) areas recognized as visually sensitive, such as National Parks, wilderness and recreation areas, coastal zones, greenbelts, conservation zones, historic districts, population centers, scenic highway corridors, and design-review overlay zones.

These areas could be more precisely defined, based on visual analysis studies, to include: specific distance zones (for example, within a half-mile foreground zone from a scenic road); particular viewsheds from key viewpoints; or designated view corridors (for example, toward nearby mountains from city parks). Some local

163

agencies have already designated a network of critical viewpoints and view corridors that require special aesthetic controls:

- Seattle, Washington, has an ordinance[1] with a list of designated public viewpoints that need to be considered in visual assessment of proposed projects, and also has a design guideline in its downtown area protecting views of Elliot Bay.[2]
- Denver, Colorado, has a city ordinance[3] that defines views to the Rocky Mountains from parks and prevents new buildings from blocking those views.
- Austin, Texas, defines numerous sections of highways around the city and corresponding view corridors that provide views of the Capitol Building to be preserved.[4]
- The county of Santa Barbara, California, as part of its Local Coastal Plan, has mapped a viewshed overlay zone along Highway 101 to protect uninterrupted ocean views.[5]

In these and many other areas under government jurisdiction, developers have to meet fairly stringent requirements, and it would be simple to add the requirement of preparing simulations from publicly acknowledged critical viewpoints. This would provide a measure of consistency for developers, and could help to reduce the uncertainties and apparent subjectivity of design review boards or vague aesthetic criteria.

There are definite precedents for such requirements. Most agencies, after all, require products such as grading plans and landscape plans as a standard part of the applicant's package. Often, there is wording that could (and probably should) be interpreted as requiring simulations but which is vague or ambiguous: words like "drawings," "photographs," "photo overlays," "graphics," and "representations" are used interchangeably or interpreted differently by different agencies, and often there is confusion over whether these graphics should show the existing site or the proposed project. For example, Section 1006.1 in San Francisco's Planning Code states:

c) Content of Applications.

. . . the application shall be accompanied by plans and specifications showing the proposed exterior appearance, including but not limited to color, texture of materials, and architectural design and detail; *drawings or photographs showing the property* in the context of its surroundings may also be required . . . (author's emphasis)[6]

As noted in Chapter 2, there are a few agencies that do explicitly require visual simulations as part of the project application or review process.[7] Often, the uncertainty revolves around the question of which projects the requirement will apply to. The news article in Figure 9-1 describes how the City of Thousand Oaks, California, deals with this issue. The same community also proposed a resolution that is more specific about the type of project for which simulations (in this case, a full-scale mock-up) would be required:

To-scale on-site building mock-up shall be prepared in conjunction with the application for major industrial projects where the total building footprint exceeds 40,000 square feet or is over 22 feet in vertical height. This shall also include demonstrating the building footprint with chalk or other method to present a clear picture of its placement within the confines of the property.[8]

Some cities require models of projects proposed in areas where a city model is maintained for planning purposes and can be continually updated. In San Francisco, Section 148 of the Planning Code states:

c) Models

In a C-3 District, in the case of construction of a new building, or any addition in height in excess of 40 feet to an existing building, two models shall be submitted to the Department of City Planning prior to approval of the project, as follows:
(1) One model of the building at a scale of 1" = 100'; and
(2) One model of the block in which the building is located at a scale of 1" = 32', which model shall include all the buildings on the block on which the building is located and the streets surrounding the block to the centerline of the streets and shall use as its base the land form starting at sea level.[6]

QUESTION: Are photo overlays a mandatory requirement to process a City of Thousand Oaks development permit, and if not, when are they required?

Photographic overlays—visual aids representing proposed buildings on specific sites—are prepared by superimposing a "to-scale" rendering of the structure upon a photograph of the site.

The photo overlay depicts the appearance of the final project on the proposed site giving Planning Commission members and other citizens an actual 'view' of the structure in its completed state.

Photo overlays are not mandatory for all projects. They are requested by the Planning and Community Development Staff Planner at a pre-application review meeting with the individual applicant, developer's design team, or owner, if deemed necessary to properly evaluate the visual impact and project's scale. Overlays are not required for most smaller buildings or structures having minimal effect on the surrounding area.

Photo overlays should be prepared only after the applicant is fairly certain that no further project changes are planned. The overlays are costly, so waiting until all changes have been made can hold costs down.

Examples of projects which could require photo overlays include major hillside projects, buildings containing unique architectural features, structures elevated more than five feet above the street; buildings exceeding 35 feet or three or more stories in height and projects containing potential visual impact on specific scenic highways and freeway corridors.

Figure 9-1. Article on simulation reproduced from the *Conejo Business Times* concerning the city of Thousand Oaks, California.

Other kinds of simulation may, more rarely, be specified. San Francisco also requires photo-simulations in its so-called "beauty contest" to judge high-rise building plans in the downtown area.[9] The city of Scottsdale, Arizona, requires a three-dimensional model, photomontage, or computer-generated perspectives of proposed downtown developments.[10] In such cases, equitable guidelines on simulation costs to be borne by the developer may need to be established. One possibility is a fixed percentage of the overall design fee for the project.

Other circumstances that may call for a simulation requirement outside designated sensitive areas might include

• Complex, unusual, or controversial projects such as power plants, new energy technologies such as wind turbines and solar collectors, office towers on the sites of old buildings, or rapid-transit systems

• Projects that are expected to result in major alterations to the appearance of the landscape, such as quarries or new motorways

It may not, of course, be necessary to require simulations from a developer. Voluntary schemes and incentives could be initiated, such as a reduced review period of exemptions from requirements where simulations clearly show that designs would be improved by such an exemption. In all cases, the preparer of simulations should be encouraged to work closely with the project reviewers in following the guidelines.

As is the case with third-party consultants hired to prepare environmental impact reports on controversial projects, agencies could require that the preparer of simulations be an independent practitioner. This could be an individual or firm hired by the agency with funds deposited by the project applicant, or any other qualified person agreed upon by the agency. On complex jobs, it may be necessary to send out requests for proposals, define the scope of work, and enter into a contractual agreement for simulation procedures and products, as is done for other professional services.

Direct Action by Local Governments

If an agency requires or encourages the use of simulations under an ordinance, official guidelines, or other policy, it must be prepared to participate in the simulation process. Minimally, its staff should be prepared to do the following:

- Participate in scoping the simulation effort and advising on or approving the viewpoints to be used, the original and presentation media, and the preparer of the simulation.
- Conduct a review of preliminary simulations and an appraisal of the final simulations, as described in Chapter 7. Agency planners, landscape architects, and architects who normally review project applications are in a position to check routinely on the quality of simulations. Simulation appraisal should be fast and simple and should flag only problems of major significance to individual project applications. Where controversy brews or hearings require expert-witness testimony, a more thorough appraisal would be justified.
- Make recommendations on actions to be taken based on the simulation appraisal. If the appraisal indicates that there is strong potential for interpreters to be confused, alienated, or misled, the agency should recommend revision of the simulations.

All regulatory agencies should also initiate a postconstruction monitoring program. This is an important and much neglected aspect of project review that would help significantly to raise the standard of simulations and the awareness of planners. Re-photography of the site, one year after project construction and at regular intervals thereafter, would reveal differences between reality and simulations of the project at various ages. These differences could arise in two distinct situations, with differing implications:

1. *Simulations may be accurate on the basis of information provided at the time, but the project was altered in its subsequent design, construction, or use.*

   Such alterations may have been approved by planning agencies. In this case, alterations expected to worsen the project's visual impact should have been portrayed in a revised simulation. If the alteration was not approved, and the deviations from the appearance shown in the simulation are serious enough, the developer could conceivably be obliged to undertake visual mitigations to bring the project into conformance with expected conditions.

2. *Simulations are inaccurate, and the project design is essentially unchanged.*

   If the simulation is seen in hindsight to have clearly created a falsely positive or harmonious image of the project, then those responsible for the simulation might in theory also be held responsible for measures to mitigate visual problems or provide compensation to affected parties, assuming that the inaccuracies were deliberate or the result of incompetence or neglect. Without strict standards for simulation, it would probably be difficult to establish this. It would, of course, also be necessary to show that the inaccurate simulation contributed to a project approval that would not otherwise have been granted on those terms.

   More realistically, documentation of this situation would be valuable in accumulating a file or reference on the kinds of inaccuracy that arise with particular projects, simulation techniques, preparers, site conditions, and so forth. Such knowledge would help simulation appraisers to detect similar problems in other simulations and to adapt their guidelines if necessary. It would also help the preparers of simulations to produce more accurate pictures, as well as forming an incentive for them to do so.

   In addition, it is important to document people's responses to the project as built, for purposes of comparison with reactions obtained from the simulations. This is the ultimate test of how misleading or fair a simulation has been. More information on this topic would allow both researchers and practitioners to make better predictions of simulation bias based on simulation characteristics.

The imposition of simulation requirements and an appraisal process raises the issue of penalties and liabilities associated with simulations that do not meet the criteria established. The penalty exacted as a result of preconstruction appraisal that reveals poor simulations is likely to be a time delay while new or improved simulations are prepared. With postconstruction appraisal, the liability increases, since if the simulations are shown to be wrong, there is potential for litigation and compensation based on professional incompetence or deliberate bias. Some cities have even begun to ask whether simulation consultants should post a bond or provide a guarantee that their simulations will be accurate. This is really just an extension of existing agency requirements that call for verification of the content of application materials. For example, San Francisco's Planning Code Section 1006.1, governing new buildings, states:

> d) Verification
>
> Each application filed by or on behalf of one or more property owners shall be verified by at least one such owner or his authorized agency attesting to the *truth and correctness* of all facts, statements, and *information presented*. (author's emphasis)[6]

In a situation where verification of simulations is required, it is clearly in the preparers' best interest to follow guidelines such as those presented in Chapter 7 as a means of ensuring against mistakes and documenting the project information they have been given for purposes of simulation. Preparers may have to prove that it was the design that changed and that their simulation was correct on the basis of information supplied at the time, in order to avoid blame for errors not of their making.

The most direct action that a government agency can take is to prepare its own simulations in-house. This has been common with agencies responsible for developing their own projects, such as municipal utilities, redevelopment agencies, and land management agencies (Fig. 9-2).

Some agencies are considering preparing their own simulations for applicants' projects. This then becomes an integral part of their

Figure 9-2. Perspective plots are routinely prepared by the U.S. Forest Service on its office-wide HP-94 computer system.

project-review process, and can avoid the risk of the applicant providing a deliberately biased simulation favorable to the project. The National Parks Service and Bureau of Land Management took this approach in reviewing the proposed Alton Coalfield, which would have been visible from Bryce Canyon National Park.[11] Some local planning agencies are planning an integrated computer simulation and geographic information system that would allow them to call up data and test design proposals for any land parcel in their jurisdiction. The use of digital data bases and video inventories stored on laser disk is beginning to allow this to happen. An active approach such as this, however, requires a substantial commitment of money and expertise. This may not be beyond an agency's resources if newly available cheaper systems are used, such as video inventory on ordinary video tape and simulation by video image processing on personal computers. Staff involved in either preparation or appraisal of simulations should receive some training and periodic refresher courses or updates in techniques of visual analysis and simulation.

PROFESSIONAL STANDARDS FOR SIMULATION

The alternative to widespread regulation of simulation procedures is a professional code of practice. If standards for simulation were adopted by professional groups such as the American Planning Association, American Society of Landscape Architects, British Town and Country Planning Institute, American Institute of Architects, and American Society of Civil Engineers, the consistency and quality of simulations undoubtedly would improve. It might even prove desirable to set up a licensing scheme; a society with wider responsibilities than architectural illustration would be of great value in broadening the acceptance of objective simulation as a planning tool. Merely the recognition of a widely accepted set of standards or guidelines of the type proposed in Chapter 7 could provide a common basis for diverse simulation applications, much as the federal agency visual-management systems provided the de facto professional standards for visual assessment in the United States in the late 1970s and early 1980s. It would also provide a firmer basis for decisions on issues of ethics and liability in preparing and presenting simulations.

REFERENCES

1. City of Seattle. 1984. Ordinance No. 111866, Part Ten, Section 25.05.902, Agency SEPA Policies, pp. 108–26.

2. City of Seattle. 1985. Land Use and Transportation Plan for Downtown Seattle. Adopted 10 June 1985, by Resolution 27281.

3. City of Denver. Denver Mountain View Ordinance (Buildings and Building Regulations), Code 1950, Article IV: Restrictions on Structures within Areas Necessary to Preserve Mountain Views.

4. City of Austin. 1984. Ordinance No. 841220-CC, Phase II, Capitol View Ordinance.

5. County of Santa Barbara. 1982. Local Coastal Plan, Section 3.4, Visual Resources.

6. City of San Francisco. 1987. City and County of San Francisco Municipal Code: Planning Code.

7. Riverside County, Calif. 1982. Land Use Ordinance 348, Article XVIII, Section 18-41. p. 221.

8. City of Thousand Oaks. 1987. Proposed Resolution No. 80-182, for M-1 and M-2 zones.

9. City of San Francisco. 1987. Rules for the 1986-1987 Approval Period of the Office Development Limitation Program (Annual Limit). City Planning Committee Resolution No. 10927. Supplement I—Submission Requirements for Preliminary Project Proposal, p. 17.

10. City of Scottsdale. 1988. Downtown Zoning Ordinance, Exhibit A, Article V — District Regulations, Section 5.3000 (D) Downtown District, p. 154.26.

11. Sheppard, S. R. J., and T. Tetherow. 1983. "Visual assessment of surface mining in the Alton Coalfield: Bryce Canyon, Utah." *Garten + Landschaft* 8(83):624-28.

Chapter 10

CONCLUSION

One of the objectives of this book is to increase people's awareness and understanding of visual simulations. Even if the word *simulation* never becomes a household name, the idea should be ubiquitous. Perhaps the name is too scientific-sounding or too long; but it does not matter what simulations are called, so long as they are used properly. One of the dangers, though, lies in too readily accepting or rejecting their use because of associations with a particular type of simulation in the past. People need to be educated to expect the use of simulations in planning and to realize that they have a choice in how simulations are prepared.

It is incumbent upon professional users of simulations to establish a much wider awareness of the importance of good simulations. There is often an attitude that illustrating the project is the trivial final phase, an extra frill added at the last moment. In fact, the development industry knows that a project can stand or fall on the basis of a presentation; why else would they pay to have sales drawings? There needs to be, at all levels, a commitment of time and money for simulation that is established at the beginning of the project approval process. Even the more sophisticated methods of simulation represent a tiny fraction of the total cost (and potential profits) of project development in most cases. It should be recognized by all parties, including the developer, that investing in fair and accurate simulations is worthwhile, so as to avoid unnecessary suspicion, argument, and delay in project review.

Those of us who are in the design, planning, and environmental professions have the responsibility of educating clients and the public about simulation; we should respond to their needs when simulation issues arise by providing sound guidance. For this to happen, we need to be better informed ourselves on the principles and implications of simulation use, even as technology rushes to outdo itself with new and advanced techniques. It is astonishing that there are, to the author's knowledge, no institutions that train professionals in the full range of typical visual simulation media and the theory and principles behind them. Those who wish to make a career or specialty out of simulation must currently choose one medium, or at the most, two, in which to train or be apprentices. Whether we wish to become experts or have no intentions of preparing simulations ourselves, we need to become more comfortable and familiar with simulations of various kinds.

There are too many myths about simulation in the minds of both professionals and laymen:

- Any picture is better than nothing
- All renderings lie
- Simulations always make things look better than reality
- All computer graphics are objective and accurate
- The simulation medium matters more than how it is used
- One picture tells the whole story
- The more detailed or elaborate the simulation the more truthful it is

Obviously, there is some basis for many of these assertions, but it is equally obvious that many of them contradict each other. The real truth is more complex. People need to look beyond the surface to judge the value of a simulation. Myths need to be replaced by solid principles. To say that all simulations lie is unfair, because it is possible to produce accurate, representative, unbiased simulations, and the guidelines presented here are intended to help achieve this. However, simulations differ from the real thing in many important ways, and users need to be aware of these differences when making decisions. Good simulations, by themselves, cannot assure good designs and good decisions—they can only help.

Research has shown that typical simulations used in the process of project approval are often unrepresentative, inaccurate, and misleading. This can contribute to a requirement for expensive mitigation measures or even to a project application being denied based on faulty information. Conversely, inaccurately portrayed projects that are approved may turn out to be an eyesore, and the opportunity to make design improvements will have been lost. The social costs of such decisions may be substantial.

It is also clear that many simulations provoke confusion and distrust among users, a situation that can itself prejudice decisions. It can encourage criticism from project opponents and cause costly delays while issues are debated or new presentations produced.

In the interests of work efficiency, cost savings, professional credibility, social consensus, and environmental quality, it is therefore important to reduce or eliminate problems due to poor simulations. Some of these problems are widely known among environmental professionals, though often ignored or exaggerated; others have never been examined in any systematic or scientific way. We do not know all the answers. The links between the accuracy of a picture and its ability to prompt unbiased decisions are complex and require further study. Guidelines and procedures, such as those suggested in this volume, deserve to be tested in both research and practice, and modified accordingly.

Meanwhile, there is clearly a need for caution on the part of those who use simulations. The validity of simulations cannot be assumed. They are already coming under close scrutiny in many communities, and creators of simulations must be prepared to select, execute, and document their methods much more carefully.

The introduction of generally accepted principles or guidelines on the preparation and use of simulations would be a major step forward. Such guidelines might also provide a basis for establishing standards of validity for simulations whenever they are used as evidence in legal cases and public hearings on emotional or controversial issues of aesthetics.

Although there is likely to be an understandable reluctance to add to the bureaucratic burden of regulations and procedures in planning decisions, improved regulation of simulations could lead to reduced restrictions in other areas. Many planning regulations such as zoning ordinances are applied as blanket policies or relatively arbitrary designations, because it is simply too complex to accommodate the infinite variety of site-specific conditions and project designs that occur. Simulations, however, can provide an enormous amount of critical information in a form that can be absorbed quickly, allowing people to judge site-specific issues more fairly. For example, it is common for local governments to control development by means of hillside protection ordinances or bulk and setback formulas; a given development may not conform technically to these restrictions, but simulations may show that it would not impact the skyline, cause long-term scarring of slopes, dominate views, or block view corridors: in other words, the project design may do none of the things that the regulations were intended to prevent, even though it would be disallowed by those regulations. By the same token, a project that technically meets the regulations can defeat their purpose due to its unregulated but more critical visual characteristics. Blanket regulations are a proxy for more informed and site-specific decision-making. We may be better off using simulations to make decisions rather than relying on imprecise regulations, so long as we can trust the simulations.

On another front, the issue of the education and ethics of professional illustrators and other creators of simulations needs to be faced. Evaluators of portrayed projects will continue to encounter problems of potential bias and attempted persuasion, so long as artistic license is actively encouraged or tolerated. Visual simulation for planning purposes is not at root an artistic endeavor. It is analogous to documentary journalism or technical reporting, rather than to storytelling. The practice, prevalent among architects, of drawing a building and then adding an entourage of plants, people, and cars is fundamentally bogus: the job of simulation is to begin with the site and show how a proposed project relates to it rather than composing the scene around the project. Design professionals must be sure to separate their creative design process from the noncreative presentation of their design in project review. Since designers avow a responsibility to both environmental quality and social good, they must strongly resist the urge to shrug off ethical responsibilities in an attempt to succeed in business by graphic deceit or negligence. At the same time, the frequency of poorly executed and unprofessional simulations must be reduced. Again, guidelines would help to achieve these goals and simultaneously give greater recognition to those professional creators who routinely produce simulations of the highest quality.

The idea of simulation appraisal should be accepted and actively put into practice. Most other professional products such as reports and plans are reviewed routinely in a preliminary or draft form before being released to the public or final decision-makers. So it should be with simulations. The time to catch problems in a simulation is before it is used and long before the project is built. No honest preparer of simulations should be afraid of an objective appraisal of his or her work.

Before leaving the subject of ethics, there are further issues that arise from the preparation of good simulations. If the project is poorly or inappropriately designed or has negative impacts, and the simulations accurately show that to be the case, there may be considerable pressure from the developer or designer not to use the simulations. The author has found himself in this situation more than once, and it presents difficult questions. Often the client will claim that the simulations, though accurate, may mislead people by focusing on the worst aspects of the project. If the simulations show only worst-case views, is the developer right in believing that people will fix on the worst view and ignore the overall or more common views to be obtained (whether or not these have been simulated)?

Sometimes the complaint is that the completed simulations, especially the precise forms of simulation, make the project look too real or too finished, when design details may, in fact, still be evolving or subject to change. In such cases, a looser, more sketchy medium may be requested instead; this may be a sign of reluctance to face real design issues or, understandably, to lock into specific solutions until general project approval has been received. Whatever the case, the situation is a frustrating and unsatisfactory one for all concerned: the preparer's simulations turn out to be, in effect, useless; the client may feel that he or she has wasted money; and an uneasy shroud of secrecy must be preserved to prevent leaking of potentially damaging information to agencies and the public.

Such cases could be avoided by two avenues suggested in these pages:

1. Clients should obtain simulations and accompanying impact assessments or preliminary design reviews early enough in the process that they can afford to change designs before sinking large amounts of money and time into them; then, a new set of simulations showing the improved design can safely be prepared and presented, and the whole process can be publicized to prove that good faith efforts have been made to develop a well-designed project. Alternatively, if the design cannot be changed, a wider range of simulations can be prepared to avoid focusing on worst-case views alone.
2. Agencies should set standards or requirements for simulation that would take the guesswork out of selecting views to be simulated, and eliminate the possibility of simulations being suppressed.

It is very important for us to know what our future landscape will look like and how our surroundings may change. With increasing public participation and design review, we can hope to influence these changes for the better. Choices may be difficult, and some argument inevitable, for our perceptions of the environment are linked to our individual associations, attitudes, and goals. We do not, however, need to have further obstacles thrown in our path in the form of doubts over the honesty of simulations, a principal tool in decisions shaping our future.

Visual simulations are a unique way to get information across to all sections of a community and to people of varying expertise who are united in having concerns for design quality and the environment. The potential of simulations as a visual communications device that can transcend cultural and language barriers while predicting environmental and social change has barely been tapped. The surest way of fostering a deserved confidence in pictures of future landscapes is to demand higher quality and consistency wherever they are used. Then, we can put our full trust in the power of simulations to help us visualize and plan future environmental changes.

APPENDIX A

TECHNICAL SUPPLEMENT

A.1. Criteria for Selecting Views to Be Simulated

Selection of Viewpoint and View Directions

- Views designated by government agencies for purposes of scenic resource protection.
- Views from sensitive use areas or important viewing areas:
  homes
  public institution buildings and civic
    spaces
  historic sites
  parks and recreation areas
  major travel and commuter routes
  scenic highways, waterways,
    trails, and bike paths
  vista points
- Views toward important or distinctive scenic features:
  mountains and ridgelines
  landmark buildings
  lakes and water features
  coastal scenery and the ocean
- Views focused or confined by:
  roadway or other travel corridor
  valley or canyon topography
  enclosing buildings or vegetation
- Views in which the proposed project would be prominent:
  on steep slopes
  on ridgelines or obstructing skylines
  in exposed areas and open view corridors
  at major thresholds (e.g., summits, bends, open spaces) along a travel sequence
- Views in the foreground approaches or entry to the project.

Selection of Viewing Conditions

- Views under recurring conditions in which the project would be seen:

    lighting (frontlit, sidelit, backlit, nocturnal)

    weather (fog, haze, dust, smog, low cloud, sun, rain, snow)

    season (spring, summer, autumn, winter)

    use and occupancy of project (traffic, people, equipment, air emissions)

    water-level fluctuations (tidal variations, high and low stream-flow variations, lake levels)

- Views at stages in the project's life when its appearance would be distinctly different:

    during construction (if protracted)

    immediately after construction (zero to five years approximately, depending on vegetation growth rates and weathering of materials)

    at maturity (five years or more, depending on the factors described above)

    during different phases of project build-out

    during or after cyclic maintenance, use, renovation, and reclamation activities

    after construction of other projects in the vicinity

Refinement of Viewpoints

Adjustments to viewpoints may be necessary to avoid on-site conditions that could be distracting or overly noticeable in a simulation that will be carefully scrutinized. Such conditions include

- Foreground objects that appear relatively large in static simulation, but that may not even be noticed in moving views from vehicles (for example, fences, street furniture, vegetation, and overhead utility lines alongside travel routes).

- Existing objects that screen or obscure part of the project from a given point but permit repeated or continuous views to a moving observer (for example, vegetation, translucent or transparent fences).

- Existing objects that artificially frame or focus views toward the project in a way that is not typical of overall views, or that forms an "artistic" composition (for example, tree branches).

- Conditions that allow more of the project to be seen than is normal in actual views (for example, short gaps in vegetation barriers).

- Existing objects that carry a symbolic message but are not a major part of the overall scene (for example, scenic highway sign in foreground, an abandoned vehicle, litter).

- Planned developments (such as foreground grading, vegetation, or structures) that would prevent views toward the parts of the project to be simulated.

- Views at right angles to or at steep angles upward from travel routes, or behind the viewer in the dominant direction of travel, unless special site circumstances encourage such views.

- Views at heights that are considerably lower or higher than typical eye level (approximately five feet for pedestrians, approximately 4 feet for car passengers), unless a slightly higher or lower level of view offers a more representative impression of overall views obtained than any single viewpoint at the correct height.

- Views from a point so close to the project that the context of the project in its surroundings is lost, unless this is an important and representative viewpoint (for example, approaching the entry to a building).

A.2. Field Recording Form for Documenting Site Photography

FIELD RECORDING SHEET							Dames & Moore

PROJECT:

LOCATION:

FIELD TEAM: DATE:

FILM TYPE:

REFERENCE MAP: EYE LEVEL RECORD:

SCALE MARKERS: SCALE MARKER RECORD:

FILM ROLL/ FRAME	TIME	LENS mm	VIEWPOINT	SUBJECT	VIEW DIREC-TION	LIGHTING (side, back, front)	WEATHER (cloud cover, brightness, shadow)

EQUIPMENT CHECKLIST:
- ☐ CAMERAS: 35 mm & Polaroid
- ☐ LENSES - NORMAL
  - - WIDE
  - -TELEPHOTO
- ☐ TRIPOD
- ☐ 35 MM FILM/ POLAROID FILM

- ☐ CAMERA CLEANING MATERIALS
- ☐ SKETCH PAD
- ☐ ABNEY LEVEL
- ☐ SURVEY ROD
- ☐ FLAG
- ☐ BINOCULARS
- ☐ ICE-BOX (FOR FILM)

- ☐ 2-WAY RADIO
- ☐ MAP(S)
- ☐ CLIP BOARD
- ☐ AERIAL PHOTOS
- ☐ ENGINEERS SCALE
- ☐ WAX PENCIL
- ☐ MEASURING TAPE

Figure A-1.

A.3. Techniques for Ensuring Simulation Accuracy

The techniques described in this section address those aspects of simulation accuracy that are hardest to judge: distortion in the image elements of position, scale, shape, color, detail, and texture. What follows is intended to help both those preparing simulations and those appraising them. A comprehensive technique for perspective drawing is not included, since there are many good texts on this subject (see Bibliography). However, some of the basics of perspective and spatial perception are necessary in order to show how proposed project designs would fit into the existing three-dimensional setting as shown in a photograph, video image, or indeed any kind of two-dimensional simulation image. Even where computers are used to generate true perspectives, the scaling techniques described here are useful in checking the reliability of the data used, the precision of the program, and the registration of wire-frames with elements in the scene. The following techniques assume that the goal is to produce a simulation that begins with the relationship of a proposed project to its landscape context, rather than generating a perspective view of the project on a blank sheet of paper and then adding in the surroundings.

Position of Objects

The position of an object in a simulation can vary in the left–right dimension, in the up–down dimension, and in depth within the scene.

Left–Right Placement

As described in Chapter 7, ("Appraising Simulations, Preconstruction"), the field of view of a simulation can be mapped by reference to landmarks or known objects in the picture (Fig. A-2). Lines of sight that on a map radiate from the viewpoint become vertical lines in a perspective view. These lines form a convenient framework for placing objects accurately within the left–right dimension. Placement within the simulation of a proposed object with a known location on the map can be determined by measuring the angle between it and some other fixed point on the map. The angle is roughly proportional to the width of the simulation,* and so, for a simulation

*This relationship is approximately correct for the central field-of-view of a normal 55 mm lens and narrower fields-of-view; it becomes increasingly inaccurate toward the edges of the image and in wide-angle or panoramic shots, where the image should really be curved around the viewer. More precise measurements of left–right position of objects in the image can be made with simple trigonometry, using the tangent of angles measured from the central line of sight to find the "opposite" side of the triangle (see Fig. A-13).

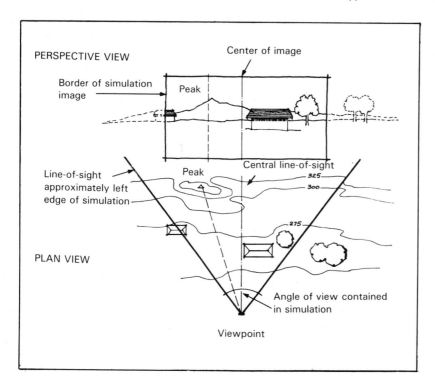

Figure A-2. Mapping field-of-view in a simulation.

image of given size, a multiplier or ratio can be established for the horizontal dimension: thus, 1 degree may equal 0.34 inches on a 16 × 20-inch image where 20 inches represents a field-of-view (horizontal angle) of 45 degrees (see Fig. A-2).

If the exact angle-of-view of the image is not known, the same technique can be applied by measuring the angles and respective horizontal image distances between two or more known points or landmark objects. If no such objects are easy to identify in the scene, it may be necessary to establish a framework of reference points by using markers such as survey rods, flags, vehicles, or balloons. Those can be placed on the exact location of the project if this can be found on the site, or at other fixed points that can be mapped accurately. Photographs then are taken from the viewpoint. Two-ways radios can be invaluable in allowing communication between the person at the viewpoint and the person marking reference points. Caution should be exercised with markers in the near foreground because the slightest error in position can throw off the calculations considerably; sensitivity to error generally falls off with distance.

The horizontal-angle technique is actually an offshoot of the conventional perspective technique, which involves locating the picture plane at the correct distance along the central line-of-sight. The simulation is the picture plane; it can be mounted on the map in some cases, allowing radiating lines of sight through certain points on the map to be projected directly onto the left-right axis of the simulation. In many cases, however, this becomes a physically less accurate process than using calculation, due to the length of the lines that have to be drawn and the graphic inaccuracy where only small-scale maps are available.

Up–Down Placement

Where topography is sloping or irregular, up-down judgments may be difficult, but they can be vital in determining the visual impacts of a project. Position can be described relative to the following critical levels:

- eye level
- horizon or skylines
- ridgelines
- existing rooflines
- lake level or sea level
- vegetation screening heights

Because of the perspective phenomenon, simple statements like "a 40-foot pole behind a 40-foot tree mass will be fully screened" cannot be accepted unless we know about the relative elevation of the base of the pole and the viewpoint. Up–down relationships can be revealed in cross sections or line-of-sight diagrams (Fig. A-3), which accurately depict the base elevations of all

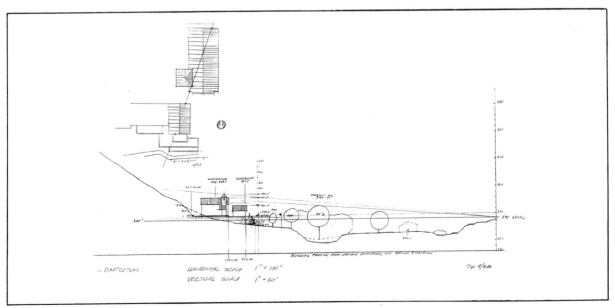

Figure A-3.   Line-of-sight sections.

critical objects. It is customary to use at least a 2 : 1 ratio of vertical scale to horizontal scale (*vertical exaggeration*), and even a 4 : 1 ratio, in order to maintain accuracy of section drawing and measurement (similarly, it is difficult to measure precisely the vertical angles-of-view in calculating elevations, because most landscapes are much wider than they are high). A drawback with line-of-sight sections is that they represent only a tiny slice of the visible scene, and many sections may need to be drawn to check accuracy in a complicated simulation. Caution should also be used in showing sections with vertical exaggeration to nontechnical people, who may be misled by the apparent height relationships.

Where objects of known elevation can be identified in the simulation image, they can be used to estimate the position of planned objects, but this should be done cautiously to take into account the vertical angle-of-view and distance effects; in particular, this is difficult where the eye level is very different from the elevation of the objects in view. Objects positioned on ridgelines, for example, may or may not appear fully on the skyline, depending upon the view angle and whether or not a "military crest" blocks views at the actual highpoints.

Eye level can be difficult to estimate in landscapes where there are no built structures having horizontal surfaces and edges. An abney level or some other survey device can be used to measure eye level in the field. This level should be recorded in the field by marking on a Polaroid photograph or sketch. In urban landscapes, it is usually easier to judge eye level and elevations by reference to the vanishing lines of horizontal building elements (Fig. A-4).

Depth

How far into the picture an object sits, with respect to the other objects, can be determined by reference to maps and aerial photographs. If, for example, there is doubt whether or not a proposed project would sit in front of or behind a clump of vegetation, then the vegetation should be located on the map and related to the location of the project. The nearer of the two objects will overlap the farther one. Without known objects or reference markers to provide depth, guesswork can be very inaccurate. It is common to underestimate the depth at which objects would be located since, as Figure A-5 shows, on flattish sites most of the image surface area is taken up by the immediate foreground (that is, at a shallower depth in the picture).

Depth of proposed objects can also be estimated if there are objects of known size at a similar viewing distance. For example, if a photograph of a particular house type is to be montaged onto a view of rolling terrain with existing houses of similar size, then there may be only one depth in the picture at which the inserted house would fit properly in terms of scale and vanishing points (Fig. A-6).

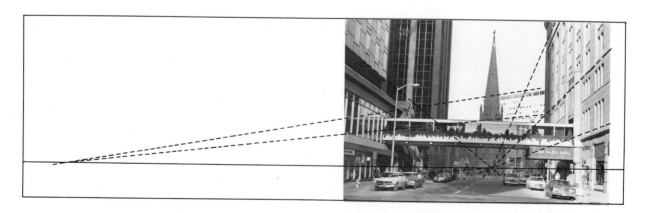

Figure A-4. Using horizontal elements in a photograph to define eye level.

20%
of
scene

50
of
scene

Figure A-5. Dominance of the foreground in a photograph.

a

b

Figure A-6. Using scale and perspective relationships to determine depth: existing conditions (*a*); insert of proposed building (*b*).

Scale of Objects

The scale or height of an object can be determined by means of reference markers and line-of-sight diagrams, as described above. Helium balloons can be tethered to the corners of proposed building footprints to mark the proposed heights in site photographs, but they are very prone to air movement, and the effect of the resulting leaning of the balloons can make it very difficult to measure heights accurately. Helicop-

ters have been used to mark the roof elevations of proposed high-rise buildings or transmission-line towers, using the instrument panel altimeter to gauge the correct height above the ground. Line-of-sight diagrams can also be used to relate the tops of objects to other features of known height (see Fig. A-3). Conventional perspective drawing techniques can be used in urban situations with flat sites.

It is possible, however, to calculate the scale of proposed objects more directly, without any markers at the project location itself, so long as other objects of known height and known location can be seen elsewhere in the simulation. This method is based on the size-to-distance relationship of objects. As the viewing distance increases, so the apparent size of objects decreases. This relationship is a simple proportional one: doubling the distance to an object halves its scale in the field-of-view (Fig. A-7). Although the relationship is proportional, the effect is that small differences in viewing distance have a much greater effect on the scale of objects in the foreground than they do on background objects (Fig. A-8).

This relationship can be used to calculate a factor or multiplier for the vertical dimension of objects in any given image. For an existing object (or reference) of known height in a particular image, the following simple equation can be used:

$$\text{vertical multiplier} = \frac{\text{image height}}{\text{actual height}} \times \text{viewing distance}$$

Thus, in Figure A-7, with tree A as a reference object and a 16 × 20 inch image:

reference image height = 3 in.
viewing distance = 1,000 ft.
reference object height = 40 ft.
vertical multiplier = 3/40 × 1,000 = 70.5

Similarly, with tree B as the reference object:

vertical multiplier = 6/40 × 500 = 70.5

Since the multiplier is a constant, it does not matter what units of measurement are used, so long as they are consistent for a given image. To be sure that the vertical multiplier is correct, an av-

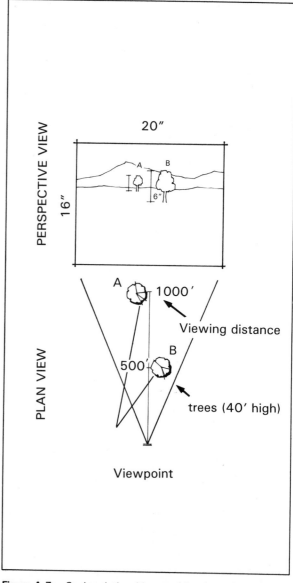

Figure A-7. Scale relationships resulting from doubling the viewing distance.

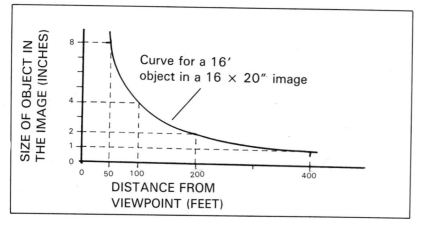

Figure A-8. Relationship of an object's apparent size to viewing distance with a given image.

erage of the calculations for several reference objects is advisable for each image. In all cases, this technique requires that the reference objects be located on the same map or aerial photograph as the viewpoint, so that viewing distances can be measured accurately. This can cause a problem if the only detailed maps available are site plans and the viewpoint is off-site, requiring different map bases to be converted to a single scale.

Once a vertical multiplier has been established for an image, it becomes simple to calculate the image height of any object at any distance, by twisting around the same equation:

$$\frac{\text{image}}{\text{height}} = \frac{\text{actual height}}{\text{viewing distance}} \times \frac{\text{vertical}}{\text{multiplier}}$$

Thus, if a structure 80 feet tall is to be built at a distance of 700 feet in the same scene as in Figure A-7, image height = 80/700 × 70.5 = 8.1 in., as shown in Figure A-9. These types of calculations can be used both to prepare simulations and also to test the accuracy of simulations where the scale of objects is in question.

The equations described above become less accurate in extensive flat landscapes and with seascapes, where the curvature of the earth exerts a strong influence, especially on distant objects. It is important to account for this in such situations by applying Bowditch's Law, which calculates the distance to the visible horizon (in nautical miles) as: $1.15 (\sqrt{H} + \sqrt{H1})$, where H = observer eye level and $H1$ = surface elevation (or height of object).

Figure A-10 describes the effect of the curvature of the earth on perspective views of marine structures such as offshore oil rigs. From viewpoints close to sea level, such effects become noticeable at relatively short viewing distances (e.g., one to two miles) and make a big difference in distant views (as shown in Fig. A-10b); the inaccuracy introduced by ignoring Bowditch's Law can lead to major visual differences.

Shape of Objects

There are various ways to ensure the accuracy of three-dimensional shapes in two-dimensional simulations. Reference markers can be located on-site to indicate corners and key features of

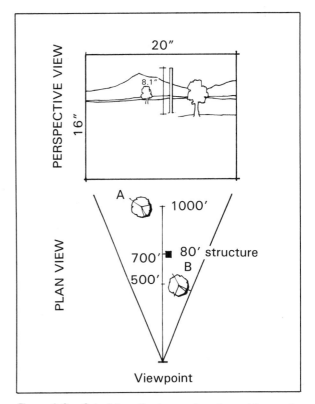

Figure A-9. Calculating the image size of an object to be simulated.

buildings, so that the simulation task becomes one of "joining the dots." Corners can also be calculated by using the horizontal-angle technique and the vertical-multiplier technique, as though they were a series of separate poles or structures.

Where the eye level is known and the project contains rectilinear parallel components (such as walls and rooflines laid out on the same grid), classic perspective drawing techniques are most useful in quickly establishing corners, heights, and vanishing lines (parallel lines which appear to recede to the eye level at vanishing points). With urban scenes, this may be all that is needed (see Fig. A-4). With less ordered landscapes, it may be necessary to calculate a few key points first, by the horizontal-angle and vertical-multiplier techniques, then derive from them the vanishing points to complete the simulation layout by normal perspective drawing.

Where more complex shapes need to be produced, the proportions (height to width) can be estimated by either the perspective drawing technique or the calculation technique. Where equal subdivision of surfaces or regular spacing of objects is required, the technique of projecting

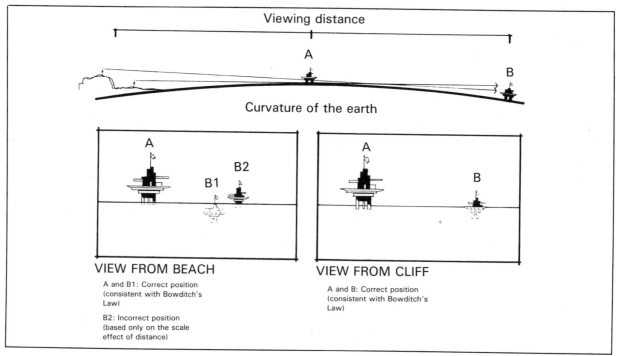

Figure A-10.   The effect of curvature of the earth on visibility of objects at sea.

parallel diagonals as shown in Figure A-11 provides useful shortcuts.

In checking the accuracy of forms and shapes, attention should be paid to their conformance with vanishing points, general proportions, orientation of surfaces to the viewer, and consistency with the project design.

Color of Objects

In selecting or appraising colors in a simulation, the qualities of value, hue, and chroma (or brilliance) all need to be considered. Decisions on accurate colors to be shown, however, need to be made in the context of the following information:

- colors and surfaces specified or described in the project design
- color balance of the overall image (especially photographs)
- lighting direction, intensity, "color temperature," and shadows, dictated by viewing conditions
- viewing distance and aerial (atmospheric) perspective

Reference to photographs of similar scenes or projects in similar conditions can be very helpful

in judging colors. If color samples of the proposed design scheme are available, these provide a starting point, but very large samples are needed to permit testing of distance effects and lighting contrast in the field.

Color *value* (lightness–darkness) can be measured by spot meters or exposure meters trained on similar existing objects, although results still need to be correlated to the range of values possible in the simulation. Felleman (Smardon, Palmer and Felleman 1986) provides a range of commonly experienced brightness levels for surfaces in different lighting conditions. Values can also be measured by comparing real or photographed surfaces with a standard gray scale, such as those produced for photography or contained in Munsell Color Charts.

Estimating tonal values of as-yet-unbuilt projects requires consideration of the intrinsic color value of the surface and the intensity of incident light, which is dictated in part by the angle of incidence (see Oles 1979). For unpolished surfaces, the more perpendicular the light rays are to the surface, the more intense is the perceived light: fully front-lit surfaces will look brighter than surfaces raked by side lighting. Shade and shadow values can be estimated by rules of thumb, as described by Oles (1979). All things being equal, the shadow cast on the ground by

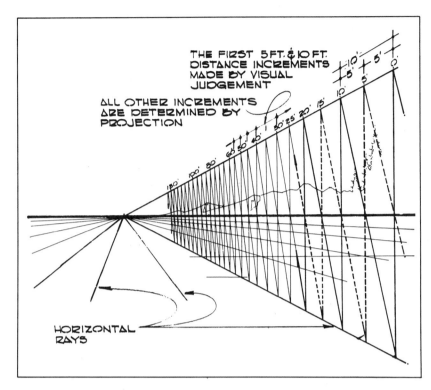

THE FIRST 5 FT. & 10 FT. DISTANCE INCREMENTS MADE BY VISUAL JUDGEMENT

ALL OTHER INCREMENTS ARE DETERMINED BY PROJECTION

HORIZONTAL RAYS

Figure A-11. Locating objects with equal spacing seen in perspective by projecting diagonals.

an object is normally darker than the shaded (unlit) side of the object itself. However, the intrinsic lightness or darkness of the ground will affect the relationship. When the sky is blue and sunlight is direct and strong, the values found for any surface in shadow are approximately midway between the sunlit surface and the darkest value possible in the picture (black). The darkness of shade and shadows also falls off with distance. The shape, length, and orientation of shadows can be constructed via perspective drawing techniques, estimated by reference to the shadows of other objects in the picture of the existing environment, or calculated by computer in generating 3-D perspective graphics. Some computer programs will calculate and depict light direction, intensities, and reflectivities for highly complex forms.

Hue refers to the color spectrum of blue, green, yellow, orange, red, and violet. *Chroma* refers to the brilliance or saturation of colors. These can be measured in real life by fairly sophisticated equipment such as photometers. More simply, Munsell Color Charts can be used to match and record the colors of materials and distant surfaces, by sighting through apertures in the charts at distant objects under the same

lighting conditions (Litton 1984). When predicting hues and chromas, it is best to obtain photographs of similar objects in similar lighting conditions at different distances, to obtain a better reading on colors and color contrasts. As a general rule, hues shift toward blue and chromas toward gray as distance increases. Atmospheric clarity and the color temperature of a particular lighting condition can exert profound influences on colors, however. Most attention should be paid to color contrasts within the simulation, since these tend to determine project aesthetics more directly than does overall color balance.

Detail and Texture

The accuracy of small-scale variations in simulated project appearance is best gauged by close comparison with project specifications. Textures and materials to be used in the design should be reviewed to identify graphic treatments suitable to match the grain or coarseness of visible surfaces. Simulated textures should undergo gradation with distance, and detail should become subordinate to massing and overall color patterns at greater distances.

A.4. Perspective Calculation Form for Manual Simulation Methods Based on Photography

Dames & Moore

PERSPECTIVE CALCULATION SHEET

NOTE: IT IS NOT NECESSARY TO COMPLETE CALCULATIONS IN ALL BOXES BELOW

PROJECT:

ILLUSTRATOR:　　　　　　　　　　　　DATE:

VIEWPOINT:

VIEW DIRECTION:　　　　　　　SPECIAL CONDITIONS:　YEAR / SEASON / VEGETATION HEIGHT

PROJECT SPECS/ DESCRIPTION:

MAP/ PLAN/ PHOTO REFERENCES:　　　　CONTOUR INTERVAL:

MAP SCALE:　　　　　　　　　　　　IMAGE SIZE:

EYE LEVEL (E/L):　　　　　　　　　IMAGE MEASURING SCALE:

SCALE MARKERS/ EXISTING OBJECTS

EQUATION: $\dfrac{\text{REF. IMAGE HEIGHT}}{\text{REF. ACTUAL HEIGHT}}$ X $\dfrac{\text{REF. VIEWING}}{\text{DISTANCE}}$ = MULTIPLIER

| DESCRIPTION | VIEWING DISTANCE | ELEVATION | | REF. HEIGHT | | HT. ABOVE/ BELOW (E/L) | | HORIZONTAL ANGLES | MULTIPLIER |
		BASE	TOP	ACTUAL	IMAGE	ACTUAL	IMAGE		

VERTICAL AVERAGE:

HORIZONTAL AVERAGE:

SIMULATED OBJECTS

EQUATION: $\dfrac{\text{AVERAGE}}{\text{MULTIPLIER}}$ X $\dfrac{\text{ACTUAL HEIGHT}}{\text{VIEWING DISTANCE}}$ = $\dfrac{\text{IMAGE}}{\text{HEIGHT}}$

| DESCRIPTION | VIEWING DISTANCE | ELEVATION | | HEIGHT | | HT. ABOVE/ BELOW (E/L) | | HORIZONTAL ANGLES |
		BASE	TOP	ACTUAL	IMAGE	ACTUAL	IMAGE	

Figure A-12.

184

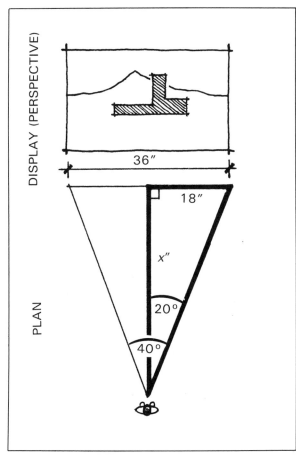

Figure A-13. Using trigonometry to calculate viewing distance for a simulation.

A.5. Determining Viewing Distance and Image Size for Presentations

The desirable viewing angle for people looking at a simulation is that which matches the actual field-of-view of the scene (see Fig. 6-10). This can be determined from the type of camera lens used, or calculated by mapping the edges of the field-of-view on a site map (see Fig. A-2).

Once the desired view angle is known and the image size required for a given presentation format has been determined, the appropriate viewing distance can be calculated. The basis for the calculation is a simple trigonometric equation (Fig. A-13). For example, for a 24 × 36-inch board showing a simulation with an original field of view of 40 degrees, the correct viewing distance (x) can be calculated by:

$$\text{Correct Viewing Distance} = \frac{1/2 \text{ simulation width}}{\text{tangent (1/2 desired viewing angle)}}$$

$$= \frac{18''}{\tan 20°} = 50''$$

For a given viewing angle, this equation can be simplified further to a ratio of simulation width to viewing distance. For example, for a 40-degree angle:

$$\text{Correct Viewing Distance} = \text{simulation width} \times 1.374$$

Thus, for a 24 × 36-inch simulation with a 40-degree viewing angle, the correct distance is 36 in. × 1.374 = 50 in. For a photograph taken with a 45-degree camera lens, the correct width : distance ratio would be 1 : 1.207.

This ratio of distance = 1.207 × image width is the basis for the viewing distances in Table 7-6.

The same equation can be modified to determine the correct image size for a room of given proportions (fixed viewing distance):

$$\text{Correct image size} = 2 \times \text{viewing distance} \times \text{tangent of 1/2 viewing angle}$$

Thus, for a room with chairs at a distance of approximately 40 feet from the projection screen, and a 40-degree viewing angle, the correct image size (y) would be:

$$y = 2 \times 40 \times \tan 20° = 29' \text{ (width)}$$

A.6. Simulation Appraisal Checklist

Project: Review Date:
Location: Reviewer:
Applicant:
Preparer of Simulations:
Preparation Date:

	Yes	No	Comments
1. *Representativeness*			
a) Are the following important views included?			
_____	_____	_____	
_____	_____	_____	
_____	_____	_____	
_____	_____	_____	
_____	_____	_____	
_____	_____	_____	
b) Are all the simulated views important or typical?	_____	_____	
c) Are typical or important viewing conditions shown?	_____	_____	
2. *Accuracy*			
a) Are simulations free of obvious inaccuracies?	_____	_____	
b) Do simulations show correct and adequate project context?	_____	_____	
c) Do simulations include all project components that would be visible?	_____	_____	
d) Do all the objects shown in the simulations conform with site plans and applicable regulations?	_____	_____	
e) Do simulations appear accurate in position, scale, and shape of project?	_____	_____	
f) Do simulations appear accurate in color and important project details?	_____	_____	
3. *Visual Clarity*			
Are simulations visually clear and understandable?	_____	_____	
4. *Interest*			
Are simulations interesting without being overly entertaining?	_____	_____	
5. *Legitimacy*			
a) Is a supporting visual analysis provided?	_____	_____	
b) Are viewpoints mapped?	_____	_____	
c) Are project design data and assumptions documented?	_____	_____	
d) Are "before" photographs provided?	_____	_____	
e) Are scale and location verifications provided?	_____	_____	

6. *Recommendations*

Accept _____   Add _____
Revise _____   Reject _____

A.7. Simulation Appraisal Forms

SIMULATION APPRAISAL FORM 1	PRE-CONSTRUCTION ____ POST-CONSTRUCTION ____	DATE: REVIEWER:

PROJECT:
LOCATION:
APPLICANT:
PROJECT REVIEW STAGE:

SUPPORTING VISUAL ANALYSIS: YES ___ NO ___

PREPARER:
DATE OF SIMULATION:
ACCOMPANYING DATA:

PRESENTATION FORMAT:
Report ____
Meeting ____

1	**REPRESENTATIVENESS**	SIMU-LATION #	YES	NO	COMMENTS
	1.1 Are the following important views included*: ___ ___ ___ ___ ___ ___				
	1.2 Are unimportant or unrepresentative views included: ___ ___ ___				

1.3 **Are typical or important viewing conditions represented:**	N/A	YES	NO	

i   Project phases or maturity
  ii Season/weather/lighting
 iii Field-of-view
 iv View sequence/duration
  v Mitigated project
 vi Project alternatives				

1.4 **Overall representativeness:**	GOOD	MAR-GINAL	POOR	RECOMMENDATION:

2	**VISUAL INTEREST** Are the simulations too lengthy, brief, repetitive, numerous, overly entertaining:	GOOD	MAR-GINAL	POOR	RECOMMENDATION:

3	**LEGITIMACY** **Is the simulation process defensible and documented:**	GOOD	MAR-GINAL	POOR	RECOMMENDATION:

	i "Before" photographs provided*
	  ii Project design data documented
	 iii Viewpoints mapped*
	 iv Scale verifications provided*
	  v Assumptions documented
	 vi Other:				

* Checking a "No" or "Poor" on these categories normally precludes acceptance of simulation.

Figure A-14. Simulation appraisal Form 1.

SIMULATION APPRAISAL FORM 2

PRE-CONSTRUCTION ___   PROJECT:

POST-CONSTRUCTION ___

4	ACCURACY	SIMULATION #						COMMENTS
		1	2	3	4	5	6	
4.1 Do simulations contain obvious inaccuracies:								
i Severe abstraction*								
ii Pronounced style								
iii Obvious errors								
4.2 Do simulations show incorrect or inadequate project context:								
4.3 Do simulations omit or contain incorrect project components:								
i Buildings								
ii Walls/fences								
iii Roads/paving/parking								
iv Grading (cut & fill)								
v Vegetation removal								
vi Landscaping - foreground								
vii Landscaping - project area								
viii Utilities								
ix Signs								
x Equipment/vehicles								
xi People/animals								
xii Water bodies/features								
xiii Dust/steam/air emissions								
xiv Glare/lights/shadows								
xv Other:								
4.4 Do simulations show incorrect								
i Position of project								
ii Scale of project *								
iii Shape/mass/outline of project								
iv Color (value, chroma, hue) of project								
v Important details/textures								
vi Other:								

4.5 Overall accuracy								RECOMMENDATION:
	GOOD							
	MARGINAL							
	POOR							

5	VISUAL CLARITY Are simulations clearly presented:							RECOMMENDATION:
	GOOD							
	MARGINAL							
	POOR							

6	RECOMMENDED ACTION							ADDITIONAL SIMULA-TIONS REQUIRED:
	ACCEPT							
	REVISE							
	REJECT							
	REPLACE							

Figure A-15. Simulation appraisal Form 2.

APPENDIX B

SIMULATION COST FACTORS

In partial response to the often asked question "What does a simulation cost?" this appendix provides information on how costs vary for certain types of simulation. Establishing unit prices for simulation is very difficult because there are so many visual and logistical variables involved in each instance. Prices also vary with regional and national labor costs. Exceptions are the rule with regard to simulation work. Where general cost estimates have been given, as in Jones and Jones (1982), they can quickly become out of date, although the relative costs of different media may be more stable. The estimated typical cost ranges given in Table B-1 should, therefore, be regarded only as a general basis for comparing costs of different approaches under the technologies, conditions, and market factors prevailing at the time of writing. They are the product of many sweeping assumptions and generalizations.

It should be remembered that regardless of medium, the first simulation will normally be the most expensive, since there may be fixed costs of fieldwork, data review, and client meetings; unit costs per simulation, therefore, tend to drop with additional simulations. Usually, the more simulations for a given project site and, especially for a given viewpoint, the lower the unit cost.

For the selected media referred to in Tables B-2, B-3, and B-4, a detailed attempt has been made to explain how and why costs vary. In each case, a standard product is assumed, the typical cost components are described, and possible causes of variation in cost are explained. The media of photosimulation, computer perspectives, and videosimulation have been chosen because they offer significant advantages in realism and/ or credibility over the more common renderings, yet are not so high-tech or expensive as to be out of reach of most simulation users.

TABLE B-1. ESTIMATED UNIT COSTS FOR SIMULATION, BY MEDIA (IN DOLLARS)

Medium	First Simulation (per project)	Additional Simulations (per project)
Rendering/sketch	500– 5,000+	400– 5,000
Computer graphic (wire-frame)	1,000– 2,500	200– 1,500
Videosimulation	1,000– 2,000	100– 1,000
Photomontage/photosimulation	1,500– 5,000+	1,000– 5,000
Model (precise)	2,000–25,000+	100–25,000+

Note: Costs exclude the one-time expense of equipment acquisition and training.

TABLE B-2. COST FACTORS FOR PHOTOSIMULATIONS (PHOTO RETOUCHING)

PRODUCT: 16 × 20-inch color prints (before and after), mounted, and labeled

Typical costs include:
- fieldwork, scale-marker measurement, and photography
- client liaison
- manual perspective calculations and documentation
- limited airbrushing (removal of objects)
- painting in (addition of objects)
- quality control
- mounting and labeling
- rephotography

Costs vary with complexity of projects:

Simple Projects   (e.g., landscaping, walls, single-pole transmission lines)

Normal Projects   (e.g., small buildings, lattice-tower transmission lines, small substations, highway modifications, dams)

Complex Projects   (e.g., new highways, large residential projects, multiple buildings, large substations, power plants)

Costs also vary with the following factors:

Factor	Higher Cost	Lower Cost
Viewing distance	close-up views	background views
Number of viewpoints	1 simulation per viewpoint	—
Mitigation/design alternatives	—	revised simulation to show mitigations or alternatives
Field of view of simulation	wide-angle (panoramic)	—
Amount of fieldwork	2 or more trips	no fieldwork required
Travel	nonlocal travel or remote site	—
Rapid turnaround	rush charges, additional labor costs, etc.	—
Amount of airbrushing	extensive airbrushing	no airbrushing required
Computer perspectives	—	plots on overlays to photographs, already prepared, reducing perspective calculation time
Incomplete project data	additional work to estimate or research appropriate information	—
Print size	24 × 36 in. or larger	11 × 14 in.
Color	—	black & white prints

TABLE B-3. COST FACTORS FOR COMPUTER PERSPECTIVES

PRODUCT:	Computer perspective plots (wire-frames) of proposed project on overlay to photograph, using a personal computer

Typical costs include:
- no fieldwork or photography (use of existing photos)
- digitizing terrain
- digitizing project
- digitizing viewpoints
- running plots
- scaling overlays to photographs
- titles

Costs vary with:

Factor	Higher Cost	Lower Cost
Number of areas to be digitized	2 or more	—
Size of area to be digitized	large	small
Complex projects	e.g., architecture, elevated highway structures	—
Inputting additional information	e.g., trees, existing structures	—
Data source	—	digital terrain data already available in a compatible format
Fieldwork	photography, viewpoint selection, etc.	—
Terrain data	higher resolution/smaller cell size	larger cell size or omission of all terrain surfaces
Location of reference points for overlay	foreground reference points, requiring very careful minor adjustments to the viewpoint and view direction	—
Number of simulations per viewpoint	1 simulation per viewpoint	2 or more simulations per viewpoint
Size of output	large overlays may require access to larger plotters or splicing of several smaller overlays	—
Field-of-view of simulation	wide-angle views may require 2 or more runs per viewpoint	—

TABLE B-4. COST FACTORS FOR VIDEO SIMULATION

PRODUCT:	Short VHS or 8 mm videotape with sequence of videosimulations showing existing and modified scenes

Typical costs include:

- fieldwork (video footage, photography, and documentation of site and similar projects)
- selection of viewpoint(s)/video images
- limited client liaison
- perspective/scale calculation
- video image processing, using images taken from other scenes
- production of edited sequence on video tape

Costs vary with:

Factor	Higher Cost	Lower Cost
Type of output	high-resolution hard copy	—
Source of footage	—	preexisting video inventory, requiring no fieldwork
Sources of images	no suitable images of similar objects, requiring ''painting'' in new objects	—
Special effects	titles, labeling, narration, etc.	—
Video format	3/4 in. or 1 in. equipment	—
Viewing distance	close-up views with foreground detail and textures	background views
Number of simulations per viewpoint	1 simulation per viewpoint	2 or more simulations per viewpoint
Travel	nonlocal travel or remote site	—
Incomplete project data	additional work to obtain required information	—

MODEL ORDINANCE AND GUIDELINES FOR SIMULATION

Model Ordinance:
Use of Visual Simulations
in Project Review

1. Purpose

The purpose of this ordinance is to set requirements and provide guidance for the use of visual simulations (renderings, photomontage, models, video, etc.) in project review. The agency recognizes that the proper use of visual simulations (hereafter termed ''simulations'') can improve the project review process in the following ways:

(i) increasing citizens' awareness and understanding of the project;

(ii) resulting in more appropriate and higher-quality project designs;

(iii) reducing uncertainty and disagreement over the project's impacts on its environment;

(iv) simplifying the project-review process; and

(v) improving agency decision-making and interpretation of existing policies.

Proper simulations are defined as pictures, models, or images that show proposed projects or future conditions in perspective views, in the context of the actual site(s), and in a manner that is comprehensible, credible to the viewer, and unbiased. In order to meet the objectives of this ordinance, simulations should be prepared and used in accordance with the standards and guidelines in Attachment A.

The ordinance is intended to encourage the use of simulations where they would improve the planning process. In particular, questions of visual compatibility with surroundings are best resolved by the use of simulations. In some cases, variances or exemptions from specific design review criteria may be granted where simulations show beyond all reasonable doubt either that

(i) the intent of the policy or design review criteria in question is met by the project design, or that

(ii) exemption will result in an improved design or reduced visual impacts.

2. Simulation Requirements

Visual simulations are required to be submitted to the agency as part of the application package for those projects that may have significant visual impacts (see Table C-1). In addition, the agency can require simulations on any project recognized as potentially having special aesthetic significance.

Simulations for such projects should be used as an integral part of the following:

TABLE C-1. PROJECT APPLICATIONS REQUIRING SIMULATIONS

Areas	Types of Project					
	Single-Family Homes	Planned Unit Development	Commercial Development	Industrial Development	Resource Extraction	Utilities Infrastructure
Parks, recreation areas	NA	NA	All	NA	All	All
Designated conservation districts, historic districts, scenic areas	All	All	All	NA	All	All
Downtown plan area	NR	Over 4 stories	Over 4 stories	NA	NA	Elevated structures only
In viewshed from designated vista points (up to 3 miles distant)	NR	Over 2 stories or 5 acres	Over 2 stories	Over 2 stories	Over 5 acres	Structures over 2 stories; linear facilities over 1/4 mile in length and requiring tree clearance
In designated green belt or coastal zone	NR	Over 20 acres	Over 2 stories	All	Over 20 acres	Structures over 2 stories; linear facilities over 1/4 mile in length and requiring tree clearance
In foreground or middleground viewshed (0–3 miles) from designated or eligible Scenic Highway	NR	Over 5 acres	All permanent facilities	All	Over 5 acres	Structures over 2 stories; linear facilities over 1/4 mile in length and requiring tree clearance
Designated view corridor or view overlay zone	NR	Over 2 stories	Over 2 stories	Over 2 stories	Over 2 stories	Elevated structures only

Note: This table is a generic example. Its definitions and exceptions should be adapted to fit each agency's situation. Definitions and categories of project types specifying minimum acreage, building height, density, etc. should be provided.
NR = Not Required   NA = Not Applicable

(i)   environmental assessment (EA), environmental impact report (EIR), or environmental impact statement (EIS);
(ii) specific development plan; and
(iii) design review.

3. Enforcement and Violations

Where simulations are provided, either under the requirements of this ordinance or voluntarily, and are found to be potentially misleading, confusing, or unconvincing, the project application may be rejected on grounds of an incomplete data submission, until such time as conforming simulations are produced. If the agency has reasonable grounds for believing that simulations have been deliberately prepared to be misleading, the project application may be denied.

The agency shall maintain a file of simulations and corresponding postconstruction photographs, as part of its postconstruction evaluation and monitoring program. This file will be made available to the public and future applicants wishing to select simulation preparers.

Attachment A
Guidelines for Use of Simulations

1. Simulation Planning

Applicants required to produce simulations are encouraged to meet with the agency prior to preparation of simulations to discuss and review their purpose, scope, and production techniques. The intent is to ensure that simulations will be representative of typical and important views, and prepared at an appropriate level of detail given the project issues and the likely audience. A supporting visual analysis is helpful in determining necessary simulation effort. Specific issues which should be determined jointly with, or approved by, an agency staff member include:

(i) project conditions to be simulated (including age of project after construction);

(ii) views and viewpoints to be used (determined in the field if necessary);

(iii) number of simulations if static images are to be used;

(iv) level of abstraction/precision in the simulations;

(v) simulation medium for the original images; and

(vi) final presentation medium and format.

Recommendations for selection of items (iv), (v), and (vi) are as follows:

(a) For projects where the agency considers that aesthetic or design issues are critical (e.g., where project may potentially cause significant adverse visual impacts, is of complex or unfamiliar design, or is the object of significant controversy), precise (detailed) simulations of high accuracy are to be prepared by an experienced simulation preparer. Suitable simulation media include detailed photosimulation; precise and realistic rendering; detailed scale models; and high-resolution solid-color computer graphics, film, or video images. Normally, these simulations should be in full color.

(b) For projects where aesthetic and design issues are not considered critical, moderately abstract simulations are acceptable, such as tonal (shaded) drawings, photomontage with some tonal variations, computer wire-frame perspectives with tonal variations added, and scale models showing vegetation and some architectural features. These simulations may be in black & white.

2. Preparation of Simulations

Simulations are to be reasonably accurate, representative, and clear in portraying the appearance of the proposed project, within the limits of the chosen views, chosen simulation techniques, and information available at the time of simulation.

(i) Simulations are to be, at minimum, accurate in the position and scale of the proposed project as depicted.

(ii) The field-of-view shown in the simulations must include sufficient site context to be representative of actual views, and should encompass a view angle not less than 45 degrees wide. Simulations should show the relationship of project to its surroundings.

(iii) Simulations must show all major project components and visually prominent features that would be visible as part of (or in association with) the planned project. These may include: major buildings, roadways, grading, utility structures, vegetation clearance, new landscaping, removal of existing structures, fences, signage, parking, vehicles, visible atmospheric effects, stored materials, and equipment.

(iv) Simulation must correspond closely with photographs or video of existing site views.

(v) Simulations must include, at minimum, tonal (shading) variations and some design details (e.g., rooflines, window locations, major new landscaping).

(vi) Highly stylized renderings or other stylized simulations are not acceptable.

3. Simulation Appraisal

Simulations are to be reviewed by the agency, or independent qualified practitioner as their designee, prior to public presentation. Intended media and formats for presentation of the simulations will also be reviewed. At the time of appraisal, the agency should be provided with a list of project design assumptions, potential or unavoidable inaccuracies, scale verifications and other perspective calculations, and other documentation enabling agency staff to complete the appraisal.

This information should be concise and simple to comprehend. Attachment B lists necessary and desirable data to be provided for simulation appraisal.

4.   Presentation of Simulations

Simulations are to be presented in a manner that is representative of actual views, accurate, and visually clear to the average viewer. Information that verifies the accuracy of the simulation should be presented. Presentations should not be too long or repetitive, nor should they be deliberately entertaining.

(i)   Presentations should follow the format agreed upon under Sections 1 and 3 above.

(ii)   A map showing viewpoints in relation to the project site must be included.

(iii)   Corresponding existing (''before'') and proposed (''after'') views must be provided.

(iv)   Alternative project designs, revised project designs, and/or mitigated project designs should be simulated where these have potentially significant effects on aesthetic quality or design compatibility.

(v)   Simulations must be clearly reproduced, labeled, and documented. Neither the simulations nor the accompanying verbal presentations should include misleading information or potentially distracting effects.

(vi)   Two-dimensional (static) simulations must be presented at a size large enough to enable viewing at the correct angle and distance (minimum 8″ x 10″ in reports, 16″ x 20″ in public presentations). At least one nonreturnable copy of these simulations, or photographs of scale models if the latter are used, must be provided to the agency to assist their review of the project.

(vii)   Video and other dynamic forms of simulation should be presented on a large screen or simultaneously on several small screens where more than ten people need to view the presentation at one time. A nonreturnable copy of the videotape, film, laser disk, or other visual data must be provided to the agency.

ATTACHMENT B.   SIMULATION APPRAISAL DATA REQUIREMENTS

1. **Basic Projection Data Used to Prepare Simulations**
   Necessary:
   - Description of the project, including structure heights, colors, and materials
   - Site plan(s) or maps preferably including grading, access roads, landscaping, and roofs
   - Project elevations and/or cross sections

   Desirable:
   - Design specifications (if available)
   - Color samples of materials (if appropriate)
   - Design assumptions where design decisions have not yet been made
   - Aerial photograph of site
   - Environmental impact report or other relevant planning/design documents, if available
   - Photographs of similar built projects

2. **Evidence of Simulation Process**
   Necessary:
   - Map(s) showing location of viewpoints and their relationship to the site plan or project features
   - Scale verification techniques, such as photographs of survey poles or other markers used in the field, or reference points surveyed/digitized

   Desirable:
   - Rationale for selection of viewpoints, or accompanying visual analysis carried out in conjunction with simulation process
   - Line-of-sight diagrams (cross sections or profiles of terrain, vegetation and structures between the viewpoint and the project)
   - Map showing angles of view used in simulations
   - Viewshed maps from viewpoints used in simulation
   - Perspective construction methods and calculations; or computer program used (with cell size and contour interval used for terrain), with source of digital data
   - Preliminary simulations (such as perspective sketches or wire-frame computer perspectives)

3. **Simulation and Presentation Products**
   Necessary:
   - Simulations themselves, preferably in the form(s) in which they will be presented (such as printer's proof or half-tone reproduction)
   - Corresponding photograph(s) or video/film of existing conditions

   Desirable:
   - Description of labels, titles, and other relevant presentation data that will accompany the simulations
   - Potential or unavoidable inaccuracies contained in the simulation (e.g., ''planned future development on adjoining site is not shown because the nature of the development has not yet been decided'')

OUTLINE OF AUTHOR'S RESEARCH

Much of the research on which the principles in this book are based was conducted by the author at the University of California, Berkeley, between 1980 and 1982. The study constituted the author's doctoral dissertation research in Environmental Planning at the Department of Landscape Architecture.

Objectives

The objectives of the study were as follows:

1. To review the type and quality of visual simulations routinely used or potentially useful for evaluating proposed projects. The aim was to document, describe, and analyze a range of simulations and compare them with the actual scenes containing the projects as built.
2. To assess whether and how landscape evaluations based on simulations differ from evaluations of the real scene; in other words, do simulations mislead people and bias their judgments, one way or another?
3. To investigate links between the nature of simulations and their effects on landscape evaluations. The purpose of this was to indicate ways in which the validity and effectiveness of a simulation can be determined before the proposed project is built. This would enable simulation problems to be detected early and be eliminated before the simulations were used in decision-making.

4. To recommend what further research is needed and whether current practice involving landscape portrayals should be modified.

Methods

The study began with a comprehensive review of simulation literature, theory, and research results. Examples of simulations and related information were then gathered. Simulations used in the study were of two kinds: working simulations, created by professionals and obtained from actual project case histories; and experimental simulations, produced by the author for the purposes of the study. The working simulations fell into two categories: those portraying projects that had subsequently been built or implemented by the time of the study, and those in which the project had not been built.

The study consisted of four major parts. Part I was a descriptive survey of the characteristics and performance of typical working simulations that portray proposed projects. It addressed the use, representativeness, and accuracy of simulations. Accuracy could be measured only with simulations of built projects, since comparison with actual views was necessary.

In Part II, three simulations selected from the sample of working simulations of built projects were manipulated to produce experimental simulations in which all variables save one were held constant. This provided controlled accuracy conditions that would enable direct relationships between specific image elements and simulation performance to be tested.

Part III obtained people's responses to both working and experimental simulations, as well as to views of the actual projects where these had been built. Part III thus provides data on bias in responses and people's appraisals of portrayal performance.

In Part IV, the data obtained were analyzed and relationships between variables were investigated. In particular, Part IV tested hypothesized relationships between bias (response equivalence) and simulation image characteristics.

Part I—Survey of Working Simulations

Part I surveyed simulations as used in practice. It described typical simulations and recorded any pertinent evidence from actual case histories on how people responded to the simulation or the built project. The representativeness and accuracy of the portrayals were appraised by the author. The appraisals of accuracy were carried out in two distinct phases. The first was an estimate, based only upon visual inspection of the simulation and reference to accompanying data on the project; this is the situation that occurs in practice—that is, preconstruction appraisal. The second was a comparative assessment based on side-by-side comparison with a view of the built project (postconstruction appraisal); in other words, it analyzed the differences and similarities between predictive simulation of the "after" scene and the actual "after" scene. Systematic routines were developed to assess accuracy in both phases.

In selecting a cross section of typical simulations, several criteria were employed:

- Various presentation formats: environmental reports, design brochures, public meetings, and legal evidence
- All commonly used simulation media: renderings, scale models, manipulated photographs of various kinds, and computer graphics (video simulations were not in use at the time of the study)
- Both full-color and black-and-white simulations
- A range of abstraction, from severely abstract to precise

- A range of landscape settings, including natural, rural, and suburban
- Various project types: residential, commercial, industrial, and infrastructure-related.

Over three hundred projects were surveyed, and from these the author was able to identify twenty-six suitable projects that had been built, and for which both simulations and the required data were available (Table D-1). Approximately half of these projects were located in California (mainly the San Francisco Bay area), and the remainder from throughout the USA. Data on the techniques employed, preparer, presentation format, etc. were documented and recorded, and actual responses to either the simulations or the built projects were noted. Color slides of each built project were obtained in the field, in conditions that matched those of the simulation as closely as possible in terms of viewpoint, view direction, time of day, season, and weather. Representativeness and accuracy of simulations were appraised (in both preconstruction and postconstruction phases) by the author using forms similar to the detailed Simulation Appraisal Forms in Appendix A.

Part II—Production of Experimental Simulations

Part II of the study involved the production of simulations in which all image properties were held constant, save one. This property was systematically varied in order to test specific hypotheses about its effect on people's responses to portrayed scenes. One hypothesis addressed the relationship between response bias in the simulation and the degree of abstraction in detail and texture of the portrayed project. A second hypothesis addressed the relationship between response bias and distortion in the portrayed color contrast of the project against its setting.

Three projects were used to develop experimental simulations, and three versions of the simulation were prepared for each project. For two of the projects, precise, moderately abstract, and severely abstract simulations were produced (see Fig. 2–19); (the abstraction extended only to the project itself; the remainder of the simulated scene was shown precisely in all versions). For the third project, value, hue, and choma were varied to create different degrees of distortion in the color contrast between project and setting.

TABLE D-1. PROJECTS IN THE STUDY SAMPLE

Project	Status: Built	Not Built	Location: SF Bay Area	Nationwide	Setting: Wildland	Rural	Suburban	Urban	Coastal	Project Type: Residential	Office Bldg.	Utility Bldg.	Power Plant	Power Line	Bridge	Recreation	Mining/Dam	Forestry	Sim. Media: Col. Model	Model B/W	Col. Photographic	Photo B/W	Col. Rendering	Toneing	Line	Col. Comput. Graphic	Comput. B/W
1 residential	•		•				•			•												•					
2 pump house	•		•				•					•												•			
3 power plant	•			•	•								•										•				
4 ski jump	•			•		•										•								•			
5 bridge	•			•			•								•				•								
6 logging	•			•	•													•						•			
7 watertank	•		•				•					•														•	
8 strip mine	•		•			•											•				•						
9 residential	•		•				•			•																	•
10 office bldg.	•			•			•				•												•				
11 playground	•			•			•									•								•			
12 dam	•		•		•												•						•				
13 power plant	•			•				•					•										•				
14 pump house	•			•			•					•													•		
15 garden/fountain	•			•												•								•			
16 power plant	•			•	•								•												•		
17 tennis club	•			•	•											•								•			
18 power plant	•			•	•								•												•		
19 office bldg.	•			•				•			•												•				
20 museum bldg.	•			•				•			•															•	
21 residential	•		•				•			•															•		
22 power line	•			•	•									•									•				
23 residential	•		•				•			•														•			
24 bridge	•		•			•									•										•		
25 power line	•		•			•								•									•				
26 office bldg.	•		•								•								•								
27 residential		•		•			•			•												•	•				
28 bridge		•		•											•							•	•				
29 office		•		•				•			•												•				
30 office		•		•				•			•												•				
31 hotel		•		•			•				•										•	•			•		
32 strip mine		•		•	•												•					•					
Totals	26	6	16	16	8	6	14	4	1	5	7	3	4	2	3	4	3	1	2	1	4	8	4	8	7	1	1

Simulation Media subtotals: Model = 3; Photographic = 12; Rendering = 19; Comput. Graphic = 2.

Part III—Testing Responses to Simulations

In Part III of the study, people's evaluations of the sample projects and their perceptions of simulation performance were sought, in order to provide information on the validity and effectiveness of simulations. Since the study was aimed primarily at the people who habitually use, appraise, and possibly create simulations for the purpose of landscape evaluation and planning, it was decided to focus upon a range of environmental professionals, including planners and designers from both public and private practice. Eight hundred invitations were sent out to professionals in these categories in the San Francisco Bay area, supplemented by an open invitation to environmental-design graduate students at U.C. Berkeley. A total of 146 people participated in the research sessions, divided into five equivalent groups. Students accounted for an average of 20 percent of each group.

The responses required from participants were of two kinds. The first were landscape evaluations, in the form of standard response scales applicable to visual analysis (such as scenic quality and visual impact). Comparisons between such responses to simulated scenes and to photographed or visited scenes permit the measurement of response equivalence.

The second kind of response comprised participants' direct appraisals of simulation quality or performance. They provide insights on the problems and acceptability of simulations, possible causes of any response discrepancies discovered, and the sensitivity of environmental professionals to variations in simulation quality.

Respondents were asked first to inspect the simulations alone and say for each simulation how confident they were that the actual scene would really look like that which was depicted. This is a measure of the credibility of an image. Confidence in the realism of the image was rated from "very confident" to "very skeptical." The reasons for the respondent's uncertainty, skepticism, or disbelief were then requested.

Next, simulations were presented side-by-side with views of the actual scene, and participants were asked to appraise the Perceived Accuracy of the simulations. This was a measure of how visually similar or dissimilar were the two views. Perceived Accuracy was rated from "very accurate" to "very inaccurate." Respondents were also asked to rate the Adequacy of the sim-

ulation in portraying the visual impact of the project in the particular view. This was an attempt to divine how important to respondents were simulation inaccuracies in influencing landscape evaluations. Adequacy was rated from "more than adequate" to "very inadequate." Respondents were asked to indicate which properties of the simulation they deemed responsible for any inadequacy.

Five presentations were organized, one for each respondent group. The same questions were asked in all presentations, using a questionnaire divided into two sections. In Section A (landscape evaluations), respondents saw a single view of each project in the form of color slides: either the site photograph of the actual view or a simulation. Once landscape evaluations had been completed for all scenes, Section B (simulation appraisals) was completed while respondents saw the same set of projects as before, now in the form of simulations side-by-side with the corresponding site photographs. One of the five groups was taken to see real views of some of the sites, instead of color slides. This group was used as a control, in order to check the validity of using color slides of real scenes as surrogates for the scenes themselves.

Part IV—Analysis of Data

The author's appraisal scores and participants' questionnaire results were tabulated. Associations were analyzed between independent variables (such as simulation subject matter, medium, type of preparer, representativeness, and appraised accuracy) and dependent variables (respondents' ratings of confidence, perceived accuracy, and adequacy, and their response equivalence in landscape evaluations). Regression analysis, analysis of variance, and chi-square tests were used. Jonckhere tests and rank-sum tests were carried out on the experimental simulations, in order to evaluate the functional relations of independent and dependent variables. Response curves (see Fig. 6-25) were drawn to compare participants' responses to simulations with equivalent groups' responses to site photographs.

Study Findings

Many of the specific results of the study are incorporated into the chapters of this book. Some of the key general findings are, nevertheless, summarized below.

Many of the "working" simulations were found to poorly represent important views of projects. Appraisals of simulation accuracy revealed that most simulations were also inaccurate, due to abstraction of the image and distortions in color, form, and project detail.

Many study participants were skeptical of the simulations, particularly those lacking detail and site context. Respondents showed most confidence in precise models and manipulated photographs. However, expressed confidence in the simulations was not closely associated with the degree of recorded bias.

Three-quarters of the simulations exhibited substantial response bias in one or more categories of landscape evaluation, although the bias was split evenly between simulations that favored the project and those that were unfavorable to the project. No strong relationship between overall accuracy (as measured) and response equivalence was discerned, although landscape evaluations varied significantly with simulation characteristics and no cases of highly accurate simulations leading to bias were found.

Some evidence was found that severe abstraction is directly related to response bias. Restricted field-of-view was found to be associated with response bias, as were various distortions of image elements such as color. The experimental simulations provided no clear evidence that abstraction of detail and texture or distortion of color contrast leads to response bias; this was probably due to the relatively minor changes in appearance of the project in comparison with the rest of the scene.

Clearly, relationships between variables are complex and a much larger sample of simulations should be used in future research to determine statistically valid patterns of association or cause and effect. Studies using the general public and decision-makers would be enlightening. Replications within subsets of simulation (for example, photomontages of office buildings) would be helpful in testing the effects of other variables (for example, accuracy in building color). Obviously, there are many possible factors that could account for the relatively low credibility and considerable bias apparently occurring in practice. This calls for caution in the use of simulation until more definitive answers can be found.

GLOSSARY

Abstraction. The omission or simplification of elements of a visual image. In **severe abstraction** all of the image elements may be omitted or simplified, and, at the most, position, scale, and general forms are indicated. In **moderate abstraction** the position, scale, forms, and tonal variations of an object in a simulation are depicted, but full color, texture, or details are omitted or simplified.

Accuracy. The similarity in appearance between the simulated scene and the real scene as it would look after the project has been built.

Aerial perspective. The effect of light-scattering and atmospheric phenomena on the perception of distant objects; usually, objects become bluer, grayer, and less distinct with increasing distance.

Animation. Dynamic simulation in which objects are seen to move or the viewer moves through a three-dimensional scene.

Background. The area of landscape farthest from the viewer, usually at a distance of several miles, where aerial perspective precludes the perception of almost all detail and texture, and only the largest forms remain prominent; often defined as the distance zone stretching from 3–5 miles to infinity.

Backlighting. A lighting condition in which the viewer is looking toward the sun and faces the shaded side of objects.

Bias. *See* **Simulation bias.**

Blue-matte process. Process used to montage two images on film; objects or action to be inserted is filmed against a blue background, and then superimposed onto the intended film backdrop which shows through only where the blue had been.

CADD. Computer-aided design and drafting, usually understood to mean automated drawing systems for laying out and dimensioning plans for proposed projects or designs in two or three dimensions.

Chroma. The purity or saturation of color; its brilliance or freedom from grayness.

Clarity. *See* **Visual clarity.**

Conceptual simulations. Abstract simulations that emphasize the underlying concepts of a design or project, and not necessarily what would be seen in real life.

Distortion. Errors in the position, scale, shape, color, detail, or texture of objects shown in a simulation image.

Dynamic simulation. Simulation that shows movement of the viewer or objects within the scene.

Experiential simulation. *See* **Precise simulation.**

Field-of-view. The amount of a scene that is included in the simulation or within the cone of vision of an observer; often interpreted as the horizontal angle of view contained within the borders of the simulation or camera frame.

Foreground. The area of landscape closest to the viewer, which can be seen in considerable detail and usually with full clarity; often defined as a distance zone of 0 to 1/4–1/2 mile from the viewer.

Frontlighting. A lighting condition where the sun is behind the viewer and the lit surfaces of objects are seen.

Generic simulation. A simulation that shows the typical appearance of a project based on general assumptions, rather than on a specific site design.

Hidden-line removal. The ability of computer graphics to render three-dimensional forms as solid masses, rather than transparent wire-frames in which all lines and edges can be seen (even those that would in real life be hidden from view).

Hue. The quality of colors (dictated by wavelength of light) that can be described as reddish, bluish, greenish, etc.

Image elements. The pictorial elements of position, scale, shape (form), color, detail, and texture, which can be used to describe all parts of an image.

Legitimacy (of a simulation). The extent to which the correctness of the simulation is demonstrated and can be defended.

Line of sight. The direct line of vision that connects the viewer's eye to the object being looked at. **Central line of sight** is the line of sight that bisects the field of view of the real or simulated view.

Line-of-sight diagram. A cross section through terrain, vegetation, and structures along the line of sight outward from the viewer's eye level at the viewpoint; it shows which objects can be seen and which would be screened or interrupted by intervening objects.

Media. *See* **Simulation medium.**

Middleground. The area of landscape beyond the foreground, in which colors, some detail, coarser textures, and overall spatial relationships are clearly seen, but finer details and textures are lost and contrasts begin to soften; often defined as the distance zone stretching from 1/4–1/2 mile to 3–5 miles.

Moderate abstraction. *See* **Abstraction.**

Munsell Color System. A color notation system that identifies the relative hue, value, and chroma of color samples, using charts with representative color chips.

Photomontage. Splicing together pieces of two photographs or a drawing and a photograph to simulate altered conditions.

Photo retouching. Altering a photograph by painting or rendering on its surface with pencils, paints, dyes, etc.

Photosimulation. A generic term encompassing all forms of manual alteration of photography to simulate a project or altered conditions; includes photomontage, photo retouching, and multiple projection.

Picture plane. The theoretical two-dimensional plane represented by the surface of a picture; in plan view, the picture plane is perpendicular to the central line of sight, and marks the point (for a plan of a given scale) where measurements made in plan correspond to measurements on the picture surface.

Precise simulation. A simulation that shows the details and complexities of a scene in a manner similar to the way the eye sees the world; a realistic (though not necessarily accurate) simulation that contains most or all of the image elements.

Realism. Strictly speaking, the degree to which a simulation is lifelike or visually accurate; more commonly used to mean apparent realism, i.e., the degree to which a simulation looks lifelike, without benefit of comparison with an actual scene.

Representativeness. The degree to which a simulation or set of simulations represents important and typical views of a project.

Response equivalence. The situation in which a simulation leads to responses similar to those obtained by equivalent observers viewing the real scene.

Scale marker. Object of known height used to provide a scale and/or location reference in a photograph or video of a site, for use in accurate simulation.

Sidelighting. A lighting condition in which sunlight comes from one side of the viewer and illuminates objects from the side, revealing both lit and shadowed surfaces.

Simulation. *See* **Visual simulation.**

Simulation appraisal. The systematic review and evaluation of the quality and adequacy of simulations, either before public viewing and decision-making, or after the project has been built.

Simulation bias. The ability of a simulation to mislead those who are viewing it, leading to responses that differ from those that would be obtained from the real project or scene. In **favorable bias**, responses to the simulated scene are more favorable than responses to the real scene. In **unfavorable bias,** responses to the simulated scene are less favorable than responses to the real scene.

Simulation interest. The degree to which a simulation or set of simulations engages or holds the interest of its audience.

Simulation medium. The simulation technique used to prepare or present simulation images; usually a combination of equipment, materials, and the preparer's or presenter's methods. **Original simulation medium** is the medium used by the preparer to create the finished original image, prior to reproduction. **Presentation medium** is the medium used to present the simulation to its intended audience, after any process of reproduction.

Solid modeling. The ability of computer-graphic perspectives to render three-dimensional forms as solid objects, usually with solid color shading and often with the effects of illumination from a light source.

Specific simulation. A simulation that shows the anticipated appearance of a project based on detailed designs and site locations.

Static simulation. A simulation that shows a still or unmoving view, as in a freeze-frame or photograph.

Tonal variation. Variation in the dark and light qualities (shading or value) of an image.

Value (color value). The relative lightness or darkness of a color.

Vanishing point. The point of convergence in a perspective view where parallel lines appear to meet or would meet if projected to the horizon; the vanishing point occurs at eye level for horizontal lines.

Video image processing. *See* **Videosimulation.**

Videosimulation. Simulation using computers to capture an image from a video frame or photograph, digitize the picture, and then manipulate or process the image to show altered conditions; two or more captured images can be combined, as a form of electronic photomontage.

Viewing angle. The angle of view subtended by a simulation image while being observed, dictated by the distance of the viewer from the image and the size of the image; ideally, the angle would correspond to the original field of view of the simulated scene.

Viewing conditions. The conditions of weather, lighting, season, project maturity, viewer motion, and other variables that affect the appearance of a scene or project.

Viewshed. The area(s) of land surface visible from a given viewpoint or viewpoints, or the area(s) of land from which an object may be seen.

Visual absorption. The degree to which the existing landscape pattern or scene can absorb landscape modifications or projects without noticeable alteration of its overall visual qualities.

Visual clarity. The degree to which the detail, parts, and overall content of the simulation can be distinguished clearly and recognized.

Visual contrast. The degree to which a project or other object would contrast with its setting.

Visual simulation. One or a sequence of visual images showing proposed projects or future environmental conditions in perspective views in the context of actual sites.

Wire-frame. Computer graphic perspectives that are composed only of lines marking the edges of forms.

BIBLIOGRAPHY

SIMULATION THEORY AND PRINCIPLES

Appleyard, D. 1977. "Understanding professional media." In *Human Behavior and Environment,* Vol. 1, ed. Altman and Wohlwill, New York: Plenum Press, pp. 43–88.

Craik, K. H. 1971. *Psychological Effectiveness of Environmental Simulations: Empirical Appraisals.* Research Technical Report. Berkeley, Calif.: Institute of Personality Assessment and Research, University of California.

McKechnie, G. E. 1976. "Simulation techniques in environmental psychology." In *Psychological Perspectives in Environment and Behavior,* ed. D. Stokols. New York: Plenum Press, pp. 169–89.

Porter, T. 1979. *How Architects Visualize.* New York: Van Nostrand Reinhold.

Schomaker, J. H. 1978. "Measurement of preferences for proposed landscape modifications." *Landscape Research* 3(3):5–8.

Sheppard, S. R. J. 1982. "Predictive landscape portrayals: a selective research review." *Landscape Journal* 1(1):9–14.

Sheppard, S. R. J. 1983. "How credible are visual simulations?" *Landscape Architecture* 73(1):83.

Sheppard, S. R. J. 1986. "Simulating landscape changes." In *Foundations for Visual Project Review,* ed. R. C. Smardon, J. Palmer, and J. Felleman. New York: John Wiley & Sons, pp. 187–99.

Zube, E. H., D. E. Simcox, and C. S. Law. 1987. "Perceptual landscape simulations: history and prospect." *Landscape Journal* 6(1):62–80.

SIMULATION TECHNIQUES

OVERVIEW OF TECHNIQUES

Burden, E. 1986. *Design Simulation.* New York: Watson-Guptill.

Bureau of Land Management. 1980. *Visual Simulation Techniques.* Washington, D.C.: U.S. Dept. of Interior.

Jones & Jones. 1982. *Substation Visual Simulation Techniques.* Portland, Ore.: Bonneville Power Administration.

PERSPECTIVE DRAWING AND RENDERING

Doyle, M. E. 1981. *Color Drawing.* New York: Van Nostrand Reinhold.

Hiss, J. B. 1985. *Perspectives: An Effective Design Tool.* Washington, D.C.: American Society of Landscape Architects.

Lin, M. 1987. *Architectural Rendering Techniques.* New York: Van Nostrand Reinhold.

Lockard, W. K. 1982. *Design Drawing.* New York: Van Nostrand Reinhold.

Oles, P. S. 1979. *Architectural Illustration: The Value Delineation Process.* New York: Van Nostrand Reinhold.

Oles, P. S. 1987. *Drawing for the Future.* New York: Van Nostrand Reinhold.

MODELS

Appleyard, D., and K. H. Craik. 1978. "The Berkeley Environmental Simulation Laboratory and its research program." *International Review of Applied Psychology* 27(1):53–55.

Janke, R. 1978. *Architectural Models.* New York: Architectural Press.

Mellander, K. 1974. "Environmental planning: can scale models help?" Institute of Urban and Regional Development Reprint No. 125. Berkeley, Calif.: University of California.

PHOTOSIMULATION AND PROJECTION

Baird, B. E., S. R. J. Sheppard, and R. C. Smardon. 1979. "Visual simulation of offshore Liquefied Natural Gas terminals in a decision-making context." In *Our National Landscape: Conference Proceedings,* ed. G. H. Elsner and R. C. Smardon. Berkeley, Calif.: U.S. Forest Service.

Day, T. R. 1987. "Simulating vegetative management techniques utilizing color photographic montage." Paper presented at the "Aesthetics of the Rural Renaissance" Conference, San Luis Obispo, Calif., August 27–29.

Penzien, J., F. J. Bindschuh, Jr., and P. R. Los. 1977. *Highway Photomontage Manual.* Report No. FHWA DP 40-1. Arlington, Va.: U.S. Dept. of Transportation, Federal Highway Administration.

Roundy, J. G., and J. A. Bohling. 1977. "A visual approach to utility planning." *Public Utilities Fortnightly* September 1977.

U.S. Forest Service. 1977. "Landscape management visual display techniques handbook." In-service manual FSH 2309-17. Washington, D.C.: U.S. Dept. of Agriculture.

WIRE-FRAME COMPUTER GRAPHICS AND CADD

Bloom, G. 1987. "New Design Dimensions." *Computer Graphics World* 10(10):36–40.

Nickerson, D. B. 1980. "Perspective Plot: an interactive analytical technique for the visual modeling of land management activities." In-service report. Portland, Oregon: U.S. Forest Service.

Orr, J. 1987. "The Next Steps for CAD/CAM." *Computer Graphics Review* 11(5):37–49.

Paulson, M. J., and R. D. Scott. 1987. "Landscape Information System: Suitability and impact modeling for industrial site selection." *Proceedings of GIS 87,* 2d Annual International Conference on Geographic Information Systems, San Francisco.

Sunwoo, P. 1979. *Perspective Plots and Photomontages for Highway Design.* Arlington, Va.: U.S. Dept. of Transportation, Federal Highway Administration, Region 15.

Twito, R. H. 1978. *Plotting Landscape Perspectives of Clearcut Units.* General Technical Report PNW-71. Portland, Oregon: U.S. Forest Service.

VIDEO AND COLOR COMPUTER GRAPHICS

Aylward, G., and M. Turnbull. 1978. "Visual analysis: the development and use of visual descriptions." *Design Methods Group-Design Research Society Journal,* August.

Danahy, J. W., and R. Wright. 1988. "Exploring design through 3-dimensional simulations." *Landscape Architecture* 78(5):64–71.

Greenberg, D. P. 1974. "Computer graphics in architecture." *Scientific American* May, pp. 98–106.

Lang, L. 1987. "Modeling the future of architecture." *Computer Graphics World* 10(10):42–45.

McComb, G. 1985. "Pictures to pixels." *MacWorld Magazine* April, pp. 68–79.

Mertes, J. D., and R. C. Smardon. 1984. "Application of video (VTR) technology in landscape planning, design, and management." In *Proceedings of Annual Council of Educators in Landscape Architecture,* Conference, Guelph, Canada, July 24–27.

Orland, B. 1986. "The image advantage: computer visual simulations." *Landscape Architecture* 76(1):58–63.

Orland, B. 1988. "Video imaging: a powerful tool for visualization and analysis." *Landscape Architecture* 78(5):78–88.

Ritchin, F. 1984. "Photography's new bag of tricks." *New York Times Magazine* November 4, pp. 42–55.

Tucker, J. B. 1984. "Computer graphics achieves new realism." *High Technology* 4(6):40–53.

West, S. 1984. "The new realism." *Science 84* July/August.

SIMULATION RESEARCH

Acking, C. A. and R. Kuller. 1973. "Presentations and judgement of planned environments and the hypothesis of arousal." In *Environmental Design Research,* Vol. 1, ed. W. F. E. Preiser. Stroudsburg, Penn.: Dowden Hutchinson and Ross.

Clay, G. R. 1986. "Assessing the utility of computer video simulations in landscape architecture." Master's thesis, University of Illinois, Urbana.

Craik, K. H., D. Appleyard, and G. E. McKechnie. 1980. *Impressions of a Place: Effects of Media and Familiarity among Environmental Professionals.* Research Technical Report. Berkeley, Calif.: Institute of Personality Assessment and Research, University of California.

Cunningham, M. C., J. A. Carter, C. P. Reese, and B. C. Webb. 1973. "Toward a perceptual tool in urban design: a street simulation pilot study." In *Environmental Design Research,* Vol. 1, ed. W. F. E. Preiser. Stroudsburg, Penn.: Dowden Hutchinson and Ross.

Schomaker, J. H. 1978. "Measurement of preferences for proposed landscape modifications." *Landscape Research* 3(3):5–8.

Sheppard, S. R. J. 1982. "Landscape portrayals: Their use, accuracy, and validity in simulating proposed landscape changes." Ph.D. diss., University of California, Berkeley.

Sims, W. R. 1974. "Iconic simulations: an evaluation of their effectiveness as techniques for simulating environmental experience along cognitive, affective, and behavioral dimensions." Ph.D. diss., Massachusetts Institute of Technology, Cambridge.

Wood, W. 1972. "An analysis of simulation media." Master's thesis, University of British Columbia, Vancouver.

VISUAL ANALYSIS AND PERCEPTION

American Society of Landscape Architects. Undated. *Visual Impact Assessment for Highway Projects.* Washington, D.C.: Federal Highway Administration.

Appleton, J. 1975. *The Experience of Landscape.* New York: John Wiley & Sons.

Blair, W. G. E., ed. 1983. "The US Practice of Visual Resource Management (VRM)." *Garten & Landschaft* 8(83):607–40.

Bureau of Land Management, 1980. *Visual Resource Management Program.* Washington, D.C.: U.S. Dept. of Interior.

Daniel, T. C., and R. S. Boster. 1976. *Measuring Landscape Aesthetics: The Scenic Beauty Estimation Method.* U.S. Forest Service Research Paper RM-167. Fort Collins, Colo.: Rocky Mountain Forest and Range Experiment Station.

Duerksen, C. J. Undated. *Aesthetics and Land Use Controls.* Planning Advisory Service Report No. 399, American Planning Association.

Elsner, G. H., and R. C. Smardon (technical coordinators). 1979. *Our National Landscape: A Conference on Applied Techniques for Analysis and Management of the Visual Resource.* U.S. Forest Service General Technical Report PSW-35. Berkeley, Calif.: PSW Forest and Range Experiment Station

Glassford, P. Undated. *Appearance Codes for Small Communities.* Planning Advisory Service Report No. 379, American Planning Association.

Hodgson, R. W., and R. L. Thayer. 1980. "Implied Human Influence Reduces Landscape Beauty." *Landscape Planning* 7:171–79.

Hopkinson, R. G. 1971. "The quantitative assessment of visual intrusion." *Journal of the Royal Town Planning Institute* 57(6):445–49.

Iverson, W. D. 1985. "And that's about the size of it: visual magnitude as a measurement of the physical landscape." *Landscape Journal* 4(1):14–22.

Litton, R. B., Jr. 1968. *Forest Landscape Description and Inventories: A Basis for Land Planning and Design.* U.S. Forest Service Research Paper PSW-49. Berkeley, Calif.: PSW Forest and Range Experiment Station.

Litton, R. B., Jr. 1973. *Landscape Control Points: A Procedure for Predicting and Monitoring Visual Impacts.* U.S. Forest Service Research Paper PSW-91. Berkeley, Calif.: PSW Forest and Range Experiment Station.

Litton, R. B., Jr. 1984. *Visual Vulnerability of the Landscape: Control of Visual Quality.* U.S. Forest Service Research Paper WO-39. Washington, D.C.: USDA Forest Service.

Lynch, K. 1976. *Managing the Sense of a Region.* Cambridge, Mass.: MIT Press.

Smardon, R. C., J. Palmer, and J. Felleman. 1986. *Foundations for Visual Project Review.* New York: John Wiley & Sons.

Smardon, R. C., S. R. J. Sheppard, and S. Newman. 1984. "Visual Impact Assessment Manual." Occasional Paper No. ESF84-009, School of Landscape Architecture, SUNY College of Environmental Science and Forestry, Syracuse, New York.

U.S. Forest Service. 1974. *National Forest Landscape Management,* Vol. 2, Chap. 1, The Visual Management System. Agriculture Handbook No. 462. Washington, D.C.: U.S. Dept. of Agriculture.

Zube, E. H., J. L. Sell, and J. G. Taylor. 1982. "Landscape Perception: Research, Application and Theory." *Landscape Planning* 9:1–33.

CREDITS

Cover: Photo by Dan Wormhoudt; Simulation by Stephen Sheppard. Courtesy of MAP Associates and Dan Wormhoudt.
Frontispiece: Photos by Stephen Sheppard.
1-1 (p. 3). Dames & Moore/David Rieseck.
1-2 (p. 4). Architectural Models, Inc. Courtesy of California Department of Water Resources.
1-3 (p. 5). Dames & Moore. Courtesy of U.S. Windpower.
1-4 (p. 5) and color **Plate 1**. Dames & Moore. Courtesy of the City of Thousand Oaks.
1-6(a–c) (p. 7). Dames & Moore.

2-2 (p. 13). Stephen Sheppard. Courtesy of Henry's, Hotel Durant, Berkeley, California.
2-3 (p. 14). Federal Highway Administration, U.S. Department of Transportation.
2-4 (p. 15). Laura Evanson, ''A new Phoenix rises in downtown Oakland,'' *The Tribune,* Oakland, California, Oct. 9, 1987: C-5.
2-5(a–c) (p. 16) and color **Plate 2**. Sir Humphry Repton. Courtesy of Environmental Design Library, U.C. Berkeley.
2-6 (p. 17). Dames & Moore. Courtesy of Sacramento Municipal Utility District.
2-8 (p. 18). EDAW, Inc. Courtesy of Platte River Power Authority.
2-9 (p. 19). Environmental Simulation Laboratory, College of Environmental Design, U.C. Berkeley.
2-10(a–c) (p. 21). Lawrence Headley, courtesy of Arthur D. Little, Inc.
2-11 (p. 22). Federal Highway Administration, U.S. Department of Transportation.
2-12 (p. 22) and color **Plate 3**. Stephen Sheppard. Courtesy of Bureau of Land Management, U.S. Department of Interior.
2-14(a) (p. 23). EDAW, Inc., San Francisco.
2-15 (p. 24) and color **Plate 4**. Alias Research/Centre for Landscape Research, University of Toronto.
2-16(a–d) (p. 25) and color **Plate 5**. U.S. Forest Service, U.S. Department of Agriculture.
2-17 (p.26). **(a)** Paul Stevenson Oles. Courtesy of I.M. Pei & Partners. **(b)** Steve Rosenthal. Courtesy of I.M. Pei & Partners.
2-18(a and b) (p. 27) and color **Plate 6**. Timothy Day. Courtesy of University of Tennessee/National Park Service, U.S. Department of Interior/State University of New York, Syracuse.
2-19 (p. 28). **(a and c)** HKS Associates; **(b)** Stephen Sheppard. Courtesy of HKS Associates.
2-20(a and b) (p. 30) and color **Plate 7**. Dames & Moore. Courtesy of Denver Regional Transportation District.
2-21 (p. 31). MBT Associates. Used by permission of Pacific Gas & Electric Co.
2-22(a–e) (p. 32). J. Alan Wagar, University of Washington, Seattle and the U.S. Forest Service, U.S. Department of Agriculture.
2-23 (p. 33). WIRTH Environmental Services (Dames & Moore). Courtesy of Montana Power Co.
2-24 (p. 34). Dames & Moore. Courtesy of Bay Area Teleport and Harbor Bay Telecommunications.

3-5 (p. 42) and color **Plate 9**. Dames & Moore.
3-7 (p. 43). Robert J. Tetlow and Stephen Sheppard. Courtesy of British Columbia Ministry of Environment (which holds the copyright for the Northeast Coal Study, Visual Resources 1976–77).
3-8 (p. 44). Devon Nickerson/Visual Simulations Inc. Courtesy of Public Service Company of New Mexico/Dames & Moore.
3-9 (p. 44). Wirth Associates. Courtesy of Arizona Public Service Company.
3-11 (pp. 46–47) and color **Plate 11**. Richard Alcina and Stephen Sheppard. Courtesy of Bureau of Land Management, U.S. Department of Interior, and with permission of the authors: R. C. Smardon, S. R. J. Sheppard, and S. Newman, 1984, Visual Impact Assessment Manual, Occasional Paper No. ESF84-009, School of Landscape Architecture, SUNY College of Environmental Science and Forestry, Syracuse, New York.
3-12 (p. 48). Peter Szasz. Courtesy of City of Walnut Creek.
3-13 (p. 49). Software and graphics by Dynamic Graphics, Inc., Berkeley, CA. Courtesy of Wagstaff & Brady.

4-1(a and b) (p. 53). Peter Szasz. Courtesy of City of Walnut Creek.
4-2 (p. 54). **(a)** Earth Metrics Inc. Courtesy of City of Sausalito; **(b)** J. Norall.
4-3 (p. 55) and color **Plate 12**. Environmental Simulation Laboratory, College of Environmental Design, U.C. Berkeley.

5-2 (p. 62). Stephen Sheppard. Courtesy of MAP Associates and Dan Wormhoudt.

6-2(a–c) (p. 66). Hartmut Gerdes, Square One Film + Video. Courtesy of Wagstaff and Brady/Robert Meyers Associates.
6-4(a) (p. 67). Sasaki Associates, Inc.
Plate 13. Stephen Sheppard. Courtesy of California Coastal Commission.
6-5(a and b) (p. 68) and color **Plate 14**. WIRTH Environmental Services (Dames & Moore). Courtesy of Tri-State Generation & Transmission Inc. and J. Wiley and Sons, from *Foundations for Visual Project Review,* R. C. Smardon, J. Palmer, and J. Felleman (eds.), © 1986.

6-6 (p. 69). (a) Scheffer Studio for Burns & McDonnell. Courtesy of Tri-State Generation & Transmission Association, Inc.; (b) Tri-State Generation & Transmission Association, Inc.

6-7(a) (p. 70). Scheffer Studio. Courtesy of Boston Edison Company.

6-8(a) (p. 71). Preparer unknown.

6-9 (p. 72). Environmental Simulation Laboratory, College of Environmental Design, U.C. Berkeley.

6-11(a and b) (p. 74). WIRTH Environmental Services (Dames & Moore). Courtesy of Montana Power Company.

6-12 (p. 75). Kathleen Seyfarth.

6-13 (p. 76). Pacific Gas and Electric Company.

Plate 15(a–h). WIRTH Environmental Services (Dames & Moore). Courtesy of Western Area Power Administration.

6-14(a) (p. 77). Pacific Gas and Electric Company.

6-17(a) (p. 80). Sasaki Associates, Inc.

6-19 (p. 81). (a) Cole/Mills Associates and Alameda County Planning Department, California. Courtesy of William Lyon Co.; (b) Preparer unknown.

6-23 (p. 84). Wisconsin Electric Power Company.

6-24 (p. 84). Software and graphics by Dynamic Graphics, Inc., Berkeley, CA. Courtesy of Wagstaff & Brady.

6-25(a) (p. 85). Hooper, Olmstead, and Emmons, Architects and Planners.

Plate 17 (a and b). EDAW, Inc. Courtesy of City of Arvada.

6-26(a) (p. 86) and color Plate 18. HKS Associates.

6-27(a) (p. 87) and color Plate 19. Kathleen Seyfarth.

6-28(a) (p. 88). State of California Department of Transportation.

6-29(a) (p. 89). Wisconsin Electric Power Company.

6-30(a) (p. 90). Wedell Group Architects and Planners.

Plate 20. Rex Barber. Courtesy of Mike Lin.

6-31(a) (p. 90). EDAW, Inc. Courtesy of Denver Botanical Garden.

6-32(a) (p. 91). John Exley/Madrone Associates. Courtesy of Marin Municipal Water District.

6-33 (p. 91). The HKS Collaborative.

Plate 21 (a). Pacific Gas and Electric Company.

6-34 (p. 92) and color Plate 22. (a) Software and graphics by Dynamic Graphics, Inc., Berkeley, CA. Courtesy of Wagstaff & Brady; (b) Stephen Sheppard. Courtesy of Wagstaff and Brady.

6-35(a) (p. 93). Environmental Science Associates.

6-36 (p. 94). (a) Wirth Associates. Courtesy of Arizona Public Service Co.; (b) Peter Szasz; (c) J. Henderson Barr. Courtesy of I.M. Pei & Partners.

Plate 23 (a–c). Dames & Moore. Courtesy of Bay Area Teleport and Harbor Bay Telecommunications.

6-38 (p. 97). EDAW, Inc. Courtesy of the National Capital Planning Commission.

6-39 (p. 97). Marin Municipal Water District.

Plate 24. Brian Orland and Charles Ehlschlaeger, Department of Landscape Architecture, University of Illinois.

6-40 (p. 98). Devon Nickerson/Visual Simulations Inc. Courtesy of Dames & Moore.

6-41 (p. 101). (a) Kane and Carruth. Courtesy of Tom Kane and Associates; (b) Jerome Sirlin. Courtesy of Kane and Carruth.

6-42 (p. 102). Devon Nickerson/Visual Simulations Inc. Courtesy of Dames & Moore and the Sacramento Municipal Utility District.

7-2 (p. 111). (a) Aariac Corporation; (b) Peter Szasz. Courtesy of City of Walnut Creek; (c) Hartmut Gerdes, Square One Film + Video. Courtesy of Gerald D. Hines Interests. Used by permission of Whitney Library of Design (Watson-Guptill Publications).

Plate 25. J. Alan Wagar, U.S. Forest Service, and Stephen Sheppard.

7-5 (p. 118) and color Plate 26. Ron Love. Courtesy of B.C. Transit. Used by permission of Whitney Library of Design (Watson-Guptill Publications).

Plate 27. Alias Research/Centre for Landscape Research, University of Toronto.

7-6 (p. 119). Chuck Cornwall/Dames & Moore.

7-7 (p. 119). The HKS Collaborative.

7-8 (p. 120). Gary J. Willmott, SUNY College of Environmental Sciences and Forestry. With permission of the authors: Gary J. Willmott, Richard C. Smardon, and Rodney A. McNeil, 1983, Waterfront Revitalization in Clayton, New York, in Small Town, November–December (1983):12–19.

7-9 (p. 120). Hartmut Gerdes, Square One Film + Video. Courtesy of Gerald D. Hines Interests. Used by permission of Whitney Library of Design (Watson-Guptill Publications).

7-10(a and b) (p. 121) and color Plate 28. WIRTH Environmental Services (Dames & Moore). Courtesy of Montana Power Company.

Plate 29. Dames & Moore. Courtesy of Arizona Department of Transportation.

7-11 (p. 126). Dames & Moore.

7-15(a and b) (p. 131). Dames & Moore. Courtesy of Denver Regional Transportation District.

7-17 (p. 132). Dames & Moore. Courtesy of Public Service Company of Colorado.

7-19 (p. 136). Dames & Moore. Courtesy of The Planning Corporation/Vista Del Mar School Board.

8-7 through 8-14 (pp. 148–152). Dames & Moore. Courtesy of the City of Austin, Texas, Electrical Utility Department.

8-15 (p. 153). City of Austin, Texas, Electrical Utility Department.

8-17(a–c) (p. 157). Keoysan Seyfarth and Associates. Courtesy of California Department of Water Resources.

8-18(a and b) (p. 158). Stephen Sheppard. Courtesy of Keoysan Seyfarth and Associates and the California Department of Water Resources.

9-1 (p. 165). Conejo Business Times, June 1986. Maria Prescott, City of Thousand Oaks Planning and Community Development Department.

9-2 (p. 167). U.S. Forest Service, U.S. Department of Agriculture.

A-11 (p. 183). U.S. Forest Service, U.S. Department of Agriculture.

1-5, 6-3, 6-10, 6-15(a), 6-16, 6-18, 6-20, 6-37, 7-3, 7-12, 7-14, 7-16, 7-18, A-2, A-7, A-8, A-9, A-10, A-13. All by Dennis Papilion.

All other simulations, graphics, and photographs: Stephen Sheppard.

INDEX